Portraits from Memory

RECOLLECTIONS OF A ZOOLOGIST

RICHARD B. GOLDSCHMIDT

Portraits from Memory

Recollections of a Zoologist

SEATTLE: University of Washington Press

Preface

THE AUTHOR begs to thank his various friends who encouraged him to publish this small volume. Professor Jane Oppenheimer, Bryn Mawr; Professor Charles Danforth, Stanford; Professor Bentley Glass, Johns Hopkins; and Professor A. R. Moore, Pacific Grove, were so kind as to read the manuscript and, in answer to a request for honest advice, unanimously entreated me to publish it. Professor Herschel Roman and others in the Zoology Department of the University of Washington were also kind enough to encourage its publication. To all of these, named and unnamed, I wish to express my sincere gratitude.

[v]

The photographs are all snapshots in my possession (some of them my own) and, as far as I am aware, have not been published before. Exceptions are the photographer's portraits of Leydig and Ishikawa.

RICHARD B. GOLDSCHMIDT

Berkeley, California
September, 1955

Contents

Illustrations

Introduction

YEARS AGO I succumbed to the urging of graduate students and fellow zoologists and presented a series of informal seminar talks on great zoologists of the past whom I had had the good fortune to know more or less well. Later I repeated a similar series while holding a Walker-Ames professorship at the University of Washington. These talks, with their reminiscing of old times and humanizing some of the great figures in the history of our science, met with a tremendous response, especially from the younger generation, far beyond the merit of the undertaking. They led also to many requests to write down their contents, requests to which I did not feel like responding while I enjoyed spending my time on experimental work. But an enforced stay away from the laboratory suggested an attempt to write down some of the material used in those talks, adding also some which I might have used. Doing so, I do not propose to give a series of well-organized biographic sketches of individuals but prefer to introduce them in a loose order, while rambling off in many directions, reminiscing on the zoological profession in Europe, mostly in Germany, at a time when most of the foundations of modern zoology were being laid and when the German universities, leading in the pioneer work, attracted scholars from all over the world—a period which ended at the time of the First World War. I beg to be excused if on many occasions I interrupt the course of my story to indulge in the pleasure of asides, to introduce little stories not connected with the main subject. When allusions made in the course of the description remind me of some interesting fact, somehow connected with the history of zoology, I simply cannot resist interrupting the yarn and intercalating, as a sort of arabesque, a topic only loosely connected, parenthetically as it were. This is of course an old writer's trick, for the use of which I ask forbearance.

1

The Background

THE REASONS why biological science in Germany was in such ascendancy in the second half of the last century are manifold. Certainly the basic cause was pure chance, namely, the appearance of men of genius who inspired their own generation and, through their students, the following generations, and who attracted men of promise from everywhere. But this is not the whole story. France, for example, produced great men who had an immense impact upon science. But their influence did not succeed in making their universities centers of scientific migration from the entire world. In addition it remained in the special field of these men and did not spread over all the sciences of life. Thus biology, especially zoology, in France and England during the time of which we are speaking (a generation after Bernard, Pasteur, Darwin, and Huxley) had many fine men but hardly produced a leader who influenced the progress of our science in its modern development since about 1870. (Perhaps Giard and Ray Lankaster came nearest to it.) Comparative anatomy and morphology, embryology and experimental embryology, cytology, protozoology, and other fields in these years had their centers of teaching and research in German universities in spite of such great figures as Lacaze-Duthiers and Delage in France, Van Beneden in Belgium, Ray Lankaster and Balfour in England, Metchnikoff and Kowalevsky in Russia, Sars in Norway, Grassi in Italy.

Some of the reasons for this situation are probably found in the specific atmosphere of the old German university. This was indeed very different from that of other countries. The condition at the basis of these differences was what the Germans called academic freedom, a term which had a much broader meaning than in its present-day usage. It included the idea of the freedom of the academicians, i.e., the students, to learn something or not to do so. There was practically no control of the student's progress, except where established in the individual laboratories as a teaching device. A student could attend the lectures for which he registered or stay away. He had not a single examination before he took his doctor's degree, with the exception of a premedical test; there were no tests, quizzes, finals, term papers, or grades. When he came up to his

[4]

doctor's examination he had to prove that he had registered for the prescribed courses but not that he had been
in attendance or had passed them. Of course this academic
freedom had its limit where laboratory or seminar work
was involved and where the professor knew all his students
as well as their actual work in spite of the absence of tests.

This system presupposed a type of university which was
completely different from the Anglo-Saxon college system.
All the teaching comprised in our ideal of a liberal education had already been done at the high school level, which
included approximately the first two years of college work.
A student who was admitted to the university on the basis
of his completion of the nine-year curriculum of the Gymnasium, a certain type of privileged high school, had finished his education in the basic fields, i.e., German, history,
geography, mathematics up to calculus, elementary sciences, and a minimum of three languages—Latin, Greek,
and French, or at a somewhat later time Latin, French,
and English, according to the type of high school attended.
The university thus was not a "school" where the student
received an education but exclusively a professional institution for the training of physicians, lawyers, all branches
of the judiciary and government, philologists, chemists,
physicists, high school teachers, and, of course, professional scholars. There was hardly a student (except the
failures) who did not stay to take his doctor's degree and
who did not afterward take up one of these professions.

Under these conditions the universities were mainly seats
of research. With the exception of the large group of law
students bent for government service, which required, in

[5]

the higher echelons, a law degree, students chose a university for a certain professor or group of professors under whom they wanted to work, and they frequently changed universities in order to receive a variety of stimulation. There was no limit to this practice except the custom of staying on, once the doctor's thesis was started, since this meant that the final choice of the major professor had already been made. Thus the majority of the students knew exactly what they wanted and worked more like fledgling scholars than like schoolboys. Only a small percentage misused the academic freedom and finally dropped out, though it was not unusual for students, happy in their new freedom after the very strict Gymnasium, to play around for a year before they began serious work. This meant simply attending longer, but since there was no set time for finishing one's studies, and even good students frequently put in an extra year for the benefit of a broader training, the older students were not very conspicuous.

A corollary to this kind of academic freedom with its dangers for the weak and character-building for the strong was the special status of the professors. One of the decisive factors resulting in the high level of the German universities at that time was the great independence of the professor and his high social position and income. Apart from the aristocracy and the officers' corps, which played a special role in a monarchy, the university professor was at the top of the social ladder. Such independence attracted strong minds and intellects and was a great background for the development of powerful personalities. This does not mean that there were no black spots to this pleasant

[6]

picture. Many of the professors became petty tyrants in their little kingdoms. Those given to vanity developed into prima donnas. The distribution by the government of honors commensurate with the social position led to rivalry for such paraphernalia as the titles of privy councilor or excellency and the different classes of decorations. Possibly the worst, almost immoral, feature was the system of remuneration, which was controlled by the government. All universities were state universities, but they were endowed with complete self-government by the faculties and by the rectors and deans, who were elected for a one- or two-year term. There were no professional administrators and there was no administration except a few clerks and book-keepers, nor was there any need for them in such a university. All professors were high civil service officers, but there was a special code which elevated them far above other government employees. First they were (and still are) entitled to retirement with full salary, originally without any age limit for retirement, and the salaries were adequate. But in addition the professor was the recipient of the student fees, a really amazing system. The students did not pay a tuition fee but paid individual fees for each course for which they registered. Around 1900, the fee for the major, standard class of six weekly lectures was forty marks per semester. This corresponded to twice the rent of a student's room or forty good restaurant dinners, i.e., about eighty dollars' purchasing power under present conditions. Almost all of these fees belonged to the professor. If he happened to be an anatomist or chemist with hundreds of hearers, he had an income equivalent to that of a

[7]

multimillionaire. But if he taught Sanskrit for a handful of students he was out of luck. What made this system worse was the organization of the different departments. There was only one full professor in each field, one zoologist, one botanist, one physiologist, etc. He gave the big lecture course of his science which all students took, and, since it was a matter of income, he had a tendency to give all other important classes, too. But how about the other professors? This was the strangest of all systems. Only the full professor received a professor's salary. All the rest of the work was done by unpaid docents!

This system deserves a more detailed description. A young man who wanted to enter the academic career had to present, about two to five years after his doctorate, a piece of research which could be considered of sufficient merit for admission to "habilitation" as *Privatdocent* (instructor). If he was accepted after some formalities, like an examination by the faculty and a public disputation which, in my youth, was still in Latin, he acquired the right to announce lecture courses and to give them, if students appeared. But he drew no salary, and since he could give only very special, not obligatory, courses which would be attended by a few interested students, his lecture fees frequently amounted to nothing. Thus in many fields only young men with independent means could enter a university career. The situation was somewhat better in the sciences. Here, besides the main classes given by the full professor, some teaching of additional subjects was needed, e.g., histology and embryology in the anatomy department; and such special classes were the booty of the younger lecturers. Moreover, in the sciences the professor had one or more assistants who helped him with the laboratory courses. These jobs were given to the lecturers, so that they drew a small salary as assistants. But there was no chance of promotion except the rare event of a vacancy and an invitation to a professorship. If no vacancy occurred, a man might be a docent for thirty or more years without any fixed income but the small fee of an assistant. After some years the government, in its great generosity, gave such men the title of extraordinary and honorary professor, but without any pay. Thus when I started my career there was in the zoological laboratory in Heidelberg, in addition to the full professor, one extraordinary professor (A. Schuberg) who was simultaneously the only assistant; there were two more such unpaid professors without even an assistant's job, both men of independent means (Lauterborn, von Erlanger). When, soon afterward, a second assistantship was established with a salary of 900 marks ($220) a year and I became the first incumbent, my chances, typical for the young scholar, were these: I might have to wait many years for a promotion from a job with eighteen dollars a month to one carrying thirty-six dollars, provided that the man ahead of me, a man in his forties, succeeded in getting a professorship. (Actually this event happened only when he had passed fifty.) During these years of waiting, I could have become docent and titular professor with a chance of picking up a few more dollars in student fees and becoming one on the long waiting list for a professorship. At this time, around 1900, most German professorships of zoology were filled by middle-aged men, with no visible chances of a vacancy and practically no possibility of the establishment of new chairs. Thus there accumulated a backlog of elderly scholars who, in spite of very respectable performance, at the age of forty or fifty still did not know whether they would ever cease to be mere assistants to a professor. This was certainly an amazing consequence of the one-department, one-professor system. It left, of course, a large number of unhappy men, and it is surprising that they still remained idealists, willing to continue with their work.

A little anecdote illustrative of these conditions may be told. About ten years after the time of my own entry into this strange race, the chair of zoology in the University of Rostock, a very small and unimportant chair, became vacant. At this time, the annual meeting of the German Zoological Society took place in Halle, and the University of Rostock sent the dean of the philosophical faculty incognito to Halle to inspect the possible candidates. Of course, soon all those in line knew of this mission. To facilitate the dean's work, Wilhelm Roux, the famous founder of *Entwicklungsmechanik*, gave a dinner party, to which the dean and all the candidates were invited. By some chance I was one of the guests, though I was still too young to be a candidate. Most probably Richard Hertwig had recommended me for the job, but success was completely out of the question. When I entered the overstuffed Victorian drawing room of Roux's comfortable house, all of the other guests were already present. I have never forgotten the expressions on the faces of the candidates, all fifteen to twenty years my elders, when I appeared. Some looked upset, some disgusted, some ready to bite me. All were very polite and affable to each other, to the host, and to the dean, while their eager minds swelled with poison, nor can one blame them in view of their hopeless situation. When we went to dinner, a very good dinner with delicious wines, everybody watched with burning eyes who would receive the chairs next to the visiting dean, which might mean that they were ahead of the others. I certainly never attended a more tense and unpleasant party, a typical result of an abominable system.

I might as well tell who won and why. The winner was Hans Spemann, who in spite of his already established reputation was, at a rather advanced age, still without a professorship, and who lived upon his private means as a docent with an empty title of professor. Actually his choice over his contemporaries was a more or less foregone conclusion, and it was due to his personality. The year before the meeting had been held at Rostock, and, as the professor of zoology was already very sick, his colleagues watched closely the proceedings and the men possibly in line. At this meeting Spemann gave the customary main address, on the problem of homology. In the discussion he was violently assailed by some of the more old-fashioned colleagues, especially by the nasty and aggressive Plate. Spemann had tried to derive his ideas from the results of experimental embryology while his opponents introduced the old-fashioned phylogenetic morphology and refused even to understand the logic of Spemann's arguments. Spemann, who on such occasions was a great fighter, defended his point by clear, cold, logical analysis, which made his adversaries still more noisy and aggressive. As happens so frequently in such situations, neither party tried to see the other's point of view, and the really exciting discussion was beginning to seem a hopeless fight when an outsider, the physiologist Winterstein, got up and made the genuine meaning of the difference crystal clear with a few extremely clever phrases. Thereupon Spemann exclaimed that he was glad that at least the physiologist understood the physiological embryologist. His statement hinted, of course, at the great fight in those days between the vitalistic experimental embryologists and the mechanistic morphologists. It was the brilliance of this discussion which secured Spemann's victory in the following year.

While we are on the anecdotal aspect of a strange organization, I might also tell how the system affected me personally, as my story is rather typical of German university life fifty years ago. When I held the glorious position of a first assistant in the Munich laboratory and at the same time an unpaid lecturer, my situation was somewhat exceptional in that the system of the student fees enabled me to make a decent living. In this large university there were many students interested in taking special advanced courses which were not given by the real professor and were therefore neither obligatory nor of any apple-polishing merit. Thus I managed to attract good numbers of students to classes on comparative histology, cytology, and later genetics and a laboratory course in comparative anatomy. But I could never be sure what my income would be, and thus the first class each semester was a terribly exciting event about which I now, fifty years later, still have nightmares. A full room would mean the butter on the bread; an empty room, dejection. I actually acquired the ability of counting my hearers and calculating the income while delivering my lecture without interruption.

What did this important transitory (but not very transitory) job of assistant to a great scholar actually mean? My own experience may serve again as an example. When I received the first greatly cherished honor of an appointment in Bütschli's laboratory in Heidelberg, he wrote me a letter explaining my duties. I was supposed to take part in the supervision of the laboratory work. This meant consulting with all the ten to fifteen students who were taking special work while doing their thesis, giving advice on techniques, checking upon microscopic work, helping to locate the literature, and sometimes assisting in the collection of material. Next I had to run the library, including the professor's private library which was accessible to the students through my mediation. I also had to take care of the teaching collection, which contained specimens of the entire animal world and a very large collection of mounted dissections, organs, and so forth, in museum jars, frequently with drawn and framed explanations. I had to fill the gaps and generally augment and improve the collection by new dissections or better mounting. Then I was in charge of the large collection of charts used in the main lectures. This also meant painting new charts where needed, as there were no funds for employing an artist. I remember vividly the time when some nosy paleontologist discovered all the segmental appendages of trilobites and I, with my mediocre gifts of draftsmanship, had to paint a chart

[13]

showing these innumerable legs in perfect left-right symmetry. There was still another duty. All specimens were
labeled with cardboard labels written in "round script." A
typewriter was an unknown piece of furniture, and so was
a secretary or stenographer. Thus I had to learn this dec-
orative script in order to write all new labels required.
Altogether I think this was quite a job for eighteen dollars
a month. I was a beginner at that time. But all the assistants in all the laboratories, many of them already scientists of standing and maturity who had not succeeded in
obtaining one of the rare professorships (there were about
twenty-four in all Germany), did the same things, though
they might have drawn up to sixty or seventy dollars a
month.

But let us now return to the doings of the full professor
and their meaning for the greatness of the German universities of that time. I believe, as I have already stated, that
the complete independence and freedom of these professors
helped considerably to attract and to develop great personalities. There was no university administration to invent
orgies of red tape with three thousand blanks in all colors
of the rainbow to be constantly filled, filed, and forgotten.
There were no committee meetings except the academic
senate. There were no secretaries, typewriters, stenog-
raphers, or reports except the annual budget-making, and
the bookkeeping was of the most primitive, household type.
Thus nothing interfered with the scientific development of
the man and his devotion to scholarship. Neither were there
so-called educators who told a professor how to teach. He
did it as he thought best, with the only limitation that cer-

tain courses had to be given. This system resulted in teaching on an extremely high level. The professor had to cover the entire field of his science in two semesters with usually six weekly lectures. These lectures were always formal lectures, well prepared and presented with logical organization and, mostly, in perfect, elaborate, and cultured language. There were, of course, good and less good lecturers. But even the less good ones did not mumble or present unorganized material or follow a textbook; they were only less good speakers. And a surprisingly large number presented brilliant lectures which inspired and fascinated the students, who, without any control whatever, did not miss a single one and literally burned the midnight oil to rewrite the lectures from their notes and to illustrate them with figures, where needed. A student who followed these so-called big lectures, meaning the main course of a field, got not only a complete survey of his science but also a glimpse into the workings of research, the difficulties of evaluation, and differences in theoretical approach, and, last but not least, he fell under the magnetic spell of a great man which influenced his subsequent life as a scientist or teacher or professional man. I am sure that hundreds of others like me, among them men from all over the world, never forgot the impression made upon their young minds by brilliant lecturers and scholars like the zoologist O. Bütschli, the physiologist W. Kühne, the chemist V. Meyer, the mineralogist Rosenbusch, the paleontologist von Zittel, and many others who taught at that time in German universities.

We have been speaking only of the teaching in one's own

field, e.g., zoology in my case. But one of the reasons for the greatness of the German universities at that time was that they still fitted their definition as *universitas littera-rum*. There was no self-respecting student, and this includes the foreign visitors, who did not devote part of his time to attending the classes of famous men in different fields. Each university boasted some such coryphaei whose classes nobody missed if possible. Thus in Heidelberg in my student days, no one, whether he was a law student, a zoology or chemistry major, or a premedical student, would miss a course with the philosopher Kuno Fischer, whose rhetorical fireworks were not only brilliant and flashy but also deep and instructive; or a course with the hypersensitive esthete Henry Thode, whose art history was one of the big attractions; or with the towering, aggressive economist Max Weber, who combined brilliancy of rhetoric with philosophical depth and the fascination of a gigantic, sensitive, and overpowering personality. To the student who was worth his mettle, such intellectual associations gave a mental experience which made his university years a power in his life far beyond the Anglo-Saxon ideal of a liberal education. Though primarily an aspiring zoologist or chemist or medical practitioner or high school teacher, he experienced at least one period in his life when he drank freely from the fountain of knowledge, flowing forth from the minds of superior intellects and personalities.

Within the sciences the professors exercised the greatest influence in the laboratories. Their courses were not meant for mass instruction but for the preparation of professionals. Thus the number of students was small enough to form a real scientific family with the professor as venerated and feared father. Students in their preparatory work, students working at their doctor's thesis, and research scholars of all ages and from many countries, working as guests, mingled in the same laboratory. The teaching was completely different from the handling of present-day mass courses. Let us look at the work of a zoology student like myself, when I entered the laboratory of the great pioneer Otto Bütschli in Heidelberg almost sixty years ago.

During the first year or so the student did not yet enter the zoology laboratory but attended the "big" lectures in zoology, botany, physics, chemistry, and frequently also geology, human anatomy, and physiology. When he was admitted to the laboratory he was supposed to be free of other major work and ready to spend most of the day there. There were no systematic laboratory teaching, special talks, or prepared material. The zoology student who took this so-called *Grosse Praktikum*, which Bütschli initiated and which was later followed in all German universities, was supposed to work through the entire animal kingdom from protozoa to mammals, each one at his own speed and at whatever times his outside work would permit. This was not a "type" course except for the vertebrates, where the cost of the material prevented taking up every single group. But otherwise every important group had to be studied, e.g., in sponges, fresh-water sponges, calcareous, siliceous, and horn sponges. Where endemic material was used, such as infusoria or hydra, the student went out to collect it. He made a study of the living material and de-

[17]

termined the species with the aid of the standard monographs. Then he made a detailed study with total mounts, dissections, and series of longitudinal and transverse sections. Thus he had to master all general and many special microscopic techniques. There were of course no technicians to take over such tasks. The present-day student will be interested to know that one of the favorite methods for total mounts and smears was acetocarmin, introduced by the early parasitologist A. Schneider—a method which was reintroduced a lifetime later. While doing all this work the student was supposed to read the classic literature on the subject and frequently also special papers when details required elucidation. In addition he was expected to make a set of perfect drawings and was not permitted to proceed to the next topic before he could show the results of his work in the drawings.

The control and direction of this work were in the hands of the professor and his assistant, though within the group discussion among younger and more advanced students was an important help. Bütschli himself made the rounds of the laboratory twice daily. This meant that he visited every single student and worked with him, sometimes for a long time. He checked upon dissections, slides, and drawings, discussed problems encountered, and also asked dangerous questions. As often as not he left behind a cigar butt, forgotten during his intense interview, to be extinguished. Sometimes he would enter the lab, assemble all present, young and old students, around the blackboard, and pose a problem—a chemical equation of biological significance to be finished or a rough sketch of some organization to be filled in. If the student who was asked failed, he got a solid dressing down. The high-strung professor, who loved all his students like a father and was beloved as such, quickly lost his temper when he met with sloppy work. I never forgot the scolding he gave me when I was to inject the arterial system of a fish and, by some clumsiness, tore off the bulbus arteriosus. Had I committed a heinous crime, I could not have felt worse. The professor also saw to it that no material was wasted; the small budget of the institute required parsimony. As a rule it took three or four semesters to finish the *Grosse Praktikum*, after which time one was ready to start a thesis, the work on which was followed by the professor just as carefully as the laboratory work. A good man could finish his thesis in a year to a year and a half during which he spent practically all his time in the laboratory except for a few special courses.

These students for the doctorate, together with visiting foreigners doing research with or without trying for a degree, meant much work for the professor, who always watched and advised daily. When I was an assistant in R. Hertwig's laboratory I was in charge of these men, and I visited daily with thirty or forty researchers in addition to the younger students and discussed their slides or counts or graphs just as if they had been my own work. Actually I overworked myself with these duties, which occupied at least half a day. At that time one came to work at 8:00 A.M. and left at 7:00 P.M.

I have mentioned that all these students were professional students. Of course only a minority could aspire to the academic career. The others, though trained to be research scholars, realized that they would have to choose to become high school teachers of biology, which meant an extra year after the doctor's degree studying philosophy and pedagogics and taking a teacher's certificate. This group of men was of special importance for the university because they were the ones to instill the scientific spirit into the youth which was to become the next generation of scientists. There were of course all kinds of teachers in the Gymnasia, good and bad ones, ordinary ones and scholars. But it is surprising how many of them kept up their scholarship while teaching school, doing some research work, following scientific literature, and frequently taking an active part in scientific societies. Many of the zoologists were active taxonomists, faunists, and ecologists. Among my school teachers was one (Reichenbach) who in his spare time did the classic piece of embryology of decapods; another one (Noll) was an authority on fresh-water sponges. One of my teachers in the classics was a recognized authority on ancient Greek geography, and this short list could be easily augmented. It was natural that schoolboys with a scientific propensity should take to such teachers, and as a result many of the boys were already imbued with the scientific spirit, in addition to possessing factual knowledge, when they entered the university. Many high school teachers gave classes in various civic organizations. In my home town there were the Physical Society, where evening classes in physics and chemistry were given by Gymnasium teachers; the Senckenberg Naturalists' Society, with classes in zoology and botany; and the *Hochstift*, with lecture courses in the humanities, art, and literature. All these classes of the adult education type were open to interested upper grade high school boys, who were thus enabled to absorb both the spirit of science and advanced factual information in their free time. Many made use of these facilities, which, at least in part, were handled by high school teachers as a highly honored avocation.

A description of the Heidelberg laboratory at the *fin de siècle* would not be complete without mentioning that typical German institution, the *Diener* (literally servant). The *Diener* was janitor, "fix-it" man, administrator of the building, laboratory boy, part technician, collector, furnaceman, confidant of the professor and the students, the fixed axis of the laboratory over a generation. He was always a former army sergeant who, after I think twenty years of service as a professional noncom, was entitled to a civil service job commensurate with his training. This meant a small but certain income for life and a pension and widow's pension in old age. All universities were state universities, and university jobs were very popular with these men because of their relative independence and also because they usually included free lodgings. Many of the *Diener* became typical fixtures of a laboratory and developed into petty tyrants, apart from their immense usefulness. The students used them as intermediaries and sources of information about the professor's mood; to the professor they were irreplaceable helpers in all the little problems of running a laboratory. When they were good, and they usually were, they knew very well their worth and considered themselves the backbone of the laboratory. Abele, the *Diener* in Bütschli's laboratory, was a husky, rough peasant who thought of himself as the material ruler of the premises. Even the professor, whom he worshiped, would not have dared to enter the laboratory on the weekly cleaning afternoon. When, as frequently happened, a group picture of the students with their professor was taken, Abele muscled his way next to the professor and planted himself squarely in the center. From the students he expected respectful treatment, which he got. In spite of the feeling of difference in rank inculcated into the old soldier, a difference which he certainly considered as ordained, he guarded the dignity of his position and never was servile, not even when accepting tips for favors. Such a good *Diener* was a great asset to the institute for which he worked as an important member. Of course, if the professor was weak, his *Diener* could develop into a considerable nuisance. While I was a student in Heidelberg, the physicist Quincke had such a factotum, who had to be present during the lecture to help carry around apparatus. When an experiment did not succeed—as happened all too frequently—Quincke addressed the *Diener* Pflug reproachfully. But the *Diener* replied in kind, and once I heard him shout at the professor, "I told you so beforehand; why didn't you hook up the wires as I told you?"

But let us return again to the university professor, the one professor in one field who was a little demigod in his surroundings. It is obvious that this exalted, independent position of the professor worked in both a positive and a negative way. Some were helped by it in developing powerful personalities of the highest order and exercised an immense influence upon their students, upon their university, and frequently upon the nation, in addition to their purely scientific performance. Less great men could become little tyrants, or glittering prima donnas, with highly developed vanity. Every university had all these types. The students were fully aware of this, made their choice accordingly, and, if they became victims of the smaller type of great men, comforted themselves with anecdotes about them which were carried through the generations. But altogether it must have been a poor student who did not come under the unforgettable influence of some really great personality among his teachers.

Professors, it is well known, are rather given to rivalries, and this was true even in the old universities, where the complete absence of an administration did not further the development of the extreme type of faculty politician. There was, of course, a little politics involved in the election of deans and rectors. But it did not amount to much and remained within the faculty in the absence of an administration. But conflicts and rivalries were not missing even without the genuine type of politician. To mention an example: the rivalry between zoologists and botanists was of long standing. There were many reasons for this. Both taught approximately the same material, in a general way, only for different organisms. Consequently each was inclined to think that the other did it less well. Thus it was not infrequent that the professor of zoology with all his students formed a militant camp against the botanist and his followers. Each group told stories about the other's weak points and was convinced of its own superiority. Sometimes this led to rather amusing situations. The following one, which involved me, is again told as a typical example of prevailing conditions. I was to take my doctor's examination with botany and physiology as minors. The zoology laboratory considered me a kind of matador who had to bring home the trophy of *summa cum laude*, and nothing less would do. But there were, from the beginning, troubles with interdepartmental jealousies. The botanist, the dull morphologist and taxonomist Pfitzer, who disliked the zoologist Bütschli's brilliance and was jealous of his popularity with the students, had used the occasion to raise a bureaucratic difficulty. I was supposed to have had a minimum of six semesters of study. Actually I had had ten, but for certain reasons I had been registered for six terms as a medical student, while taking only science classes and premedical ones which were all in science. Professor Pfitzer himself had given me the premedical examination in botany, which I had passed with the grade A. Nevertheless he contended that I could not be admitted with only four terms of science. This attitude was of course pure chicanery directed against my sponsor, Bütschli. The faculty, however, accepted me, a defeat which Pfitzer kept in mind.

The day of the examination came. At that time, in Heidelberg, this was quite a strange affair. After the thesis had been approved, the candidate for the doctor's degree had to appear in the morning, at about eleven o'clock, in tails, hard-boiled shirt, white necktie, the high collar called appropriately a *Vatermörder*, white leather gloves, and a silk hat. The professors wore their business suits. First the major professor examined for one hour, and later the two minors took half an hour each. In between there was a very important intermission during which the dean had to provide wine and sandwiches. Every professor was entitled to attend any doctor's examination if he wanted. If it was known that the dean was a connoisseur of good wines, the whole faculty appeared at intermission time to enjoy the free treat and to chat. The poor candidate in his stiff collar stood completely neglected in a corner, not daring to touch the wine, and the only one around with a serious face. This was quite an ordeal.

Now it must be recorded that the botanist Pfitzer had a favorite subject commensurate with his pedantic mind— the difference between thorns and spines. The popular saying, "There is no rose without thorns," is false because a rose has no thorns but spines (dermal products), while the hawthorn has thorns (transformed stems). The pedant never gave an examination without asking about this piece of morphology. Like every student I was prepared for this question, and, true, it was the first thing Pfitzer asked. But there must have been a gremlin in my cockpit. I answered giving the definition of thorn for spine and vice versa. Pfitzer looked deeply insulted, bit his lips, and all but fainted. With subdued and reproachful voice he continued for the prescribed half hour, asking me questions, all of which I answered. Then he dismissed me with the grade C, which was the end of my hope for *summa cum laude*.

Bütschli took this as a personal insult, which it was meant to be, and fumed. But every dog has his day, and mine came soon. It was a rule that on the morning following his examination the newly baked doctor again donned his tails and all the rest and called upon his three examiners to thank them for their share. Thus I went to Pfitzer to make the solemn call. After I was seated, he said in a sanctimonious voice, "Well, the examination went off quite well, in view of the short time you were a student in our faculty." I answered, "I think, Mr. Professor, I found a thorn in it . . . oh, excuse me, I mean . . . a spine." With this I left, returned at once to the zoological institute, and told Bütschli what had happened. He roared with laughter and repeated the proverb, "He who laughs last laughs best."

This memorable doctor's examination even started in a remarkable way. In the morning, before dressing for the ordeal, I took a walk along the charming banks of the Neckar River to soothe my jangling nerves. Returning I met a fellow student, E. Zugmayer (later an explorer of Tibet), who had just attended Bütschli's morning lecture in which he had spoken of brachiopods. As a joke Zugmayer, who was a Viennese full of fun, assumed Bütschli's voice and addressed me, "Mr. Candidate, what do you know about the development of brachiopods?" With horror I had to state that I did not know much, whereupon Zugmayer told me all he had just learned in the lecture. Two hours later I sat opposite Bütschli, who started my examination with the words, "Mr. Candidate, what do you know about the development of brachiopods?"

This is not yet the entire story of how my examination reflected professorial narrowness. My second minor was physiology, the examiner the great biochemist A. Kossel, who was professor of physiology after the brilliant Wilhelm Kühne, my first teacher. Physiology belonged to the medical faculty, and therefore I had to receive special permission to take it as a minor in a science faculty doctorate. This led again to conflicts. The chemist Curtius especially opposed my request, as he wanted to keep the monopoly on chemistry and, in addition, considered Kossel's biochemistry a kind of amateurish doings of a medical man. Finally it was agreed that I could take physiology, but that this was not to be considered a precedent for future cases. Kossel, as professor of physiology, had to lecture on all of human physiology. But of course the field of his own research, biochemistry (at that time called chemical physiology), stood easily in the foreground of his interest. Thus I expected to be examined preponderantly in chemical physiology and had carefully prepared this field. When Kossel's turn came to examine me, suddenly Curtius entered and with his immense bulk and the ruddy face of the tippler sat down next to Kossel, obviously intending to find out what kind of second-rate chemistry would be produced. This angered Kossel, and he examined me for his half hour exclusively on the special physiology of the head nerves, without asking a single chemical question. I am certain that he was very little at home with the subject he examined, but, unfortunately, he was still better than his victim, myself. Thus this doctor's examination ended with everybody angry: Bütschli because of the doings of Pfitzer and Curtius which had damaged the record of one of his favorite students; Pfitzer because the candidate had insulted him by mixing up thorns and spines; Kossel because of Curtius' rude interference; Curtius because Kossel had got the better of him; and, finally, myself for all too obvious reasons.

But on my side this was soon forgotten. Outside the university waited the whole zoological laboratory, with the janitor carrying a flag, and we marched to one of the cozy old wine joints where, according to tradition, I treated the whole gang to the *Doktorschmaus*, a banquet with an unlimited flow of good domestic wine.

2

Survivors from Darwin's Days

W<small>HEN I STARTED</small> my study of zoology in
1896, the great masters of the time were the men who had
established their fame between 1870 and 1880, when the
foundations of cytology, protozoology, and much of embryology and comparative anatomy were laid. They were
the students who stood upon the shoulders of the great
zoologists who, after Von Baer, Schleiden and Schwann,
Cuvier, Lamarck, and Geoffroy Saint-Hilaire, had begun
to lay the foundations of microscopic anatomy based
upon the cell theory, and of embryology and comparative
anatomy in the light of evolution. Apart from Darwin
and Huxley in England and Claude Bernard, Pasteur,

and the histologist Ranvier in France, the strongest influence had been exercised by the physiologist and zoologist Johannes Müller, the ancestor of the greatest school of zoologists in Germany, and further by the embryologists Remak and His; the zoologists, histologists, and all-around morphologists Leydig and Kölliker; the German counterpart of Huxley in matters of evolution, Haeckel; the discoverer of the life cycles of parasites, and taxonomist on a grand scale, Leuckart; to mention only the founders of great schools. Of this group of classicists a few were still alive, and it is pleasant to remember that I had a fleeting glimpse of some of them and more than this of others.

Franz Leydig and Albert von Kölliker

The two men whom I saw at least from an admiring distance were Leydig and Kölliker. Leydig, whose name survives in the Leydig cells and the Leydig substance, had been professor in Bonn, where he did his great work in so many fields of microscopic anatomy. In his old days he retired to the romantic medieval city of Rothenburg, where he lived, practically without contact with the rest of the world, in a small, old, white-washed cottage outside the city walls. When the German zoologists met in Würzburg in 1903, a kind of pilgrimage was arranged to Rothenburg to visit the octogenarian, and I was one of the party. Only our leader, Boveri, was admitted to the house, but soon afterward Leydig came out to greet us and to shake hands with everybody. I remember well the noble bearing of the grand old man. He wore a simple black suit which contrasted with his snow-white hair and long, silky beard. His dark eyes were full of life, and though not much was spoken I was greatly impressed with the scene. A few weeks later all of us received his signed photograph, which still hangs in my laboratory.

Kölliker, who was also an octogenarian when I saw him, was still full of activity. I met him at a meeting of the anatomists' society over which he presided. He sat or stood through all the papers, performed his presidential duties, and took part frequently in discussions in a clear, mild voice. He was one of the most beautiful old men I have ever seen. He had a large head with a handsome arched forehead framed by rather long, smooth, white hair. A small white mustache enhanced the finely cut profile, and his whole bearing, of a modest nobility, was immensely impressive, so much so that I could still draw his portrait from memory, if I possessed that gift.

Ernst Haeckel
Aside: L. PLATE

I had the good luck to see a little more of Ernst Haeckel, one of the most amazing and most controversial figures German science has produced. The present generation cannot imagine the role he played in his time, far beyond his actual scientific performance. Haeckel was one of the students of Johannes Müller and thus the first to help in founding the dynasty of zoologists, already mentioned, near the end of which I find myself. Like most zoologists of those days he studied medicine, and he took his M.D. with a thesis containing a great discovery: the amoeboid movement of the lymphocytes (in the blood of the crayfish). He hung out his shingle, and, when it turned out that no patients appeared at the visiting hours from 7:00 to 8:00 A.M., he gave up and became what he wanted to be, a zoologist. Johannes Müller had initiated his students into marine zoology. He loved to go to the Mediterranean, settle in some fishing village, hire a boat and an empty shack as a laboratory, and start a study of the rich treasures which were to be found all around. Haeckel chose the study of the medusae and later of the radiolaria. His big monographs on these groups are still basic for their taxonomy and morphology. They are actually almost the only factual contributions Haeckel made to zoology, enough to secure him a professorship in Jena but not enough for his later fame, which was based upon a completely different performance.

In this, his morphological and taxonomic work, Haeckel already showed a gift and a tendency which were to get him into trouble later. He had a great facility in draftsmanship and for some time had thought of becoming a painter. As a matter of fact, he would have been a very poor Victorian painter, as can be seen from samples of his work, some of which he published with his travel books on Ceylon and Java. Others I saw in his house. They were mere illustrations, well executed but completely conventional and uninteresting and without any artistic merit. Actually Haeckel, in his later life, had a chance to demonstrate his lack of genuine artistic feeling when he violently opposed the frescoes which the great Swiss Ernst Hodler painted for the University in Jena, his admirable "Departure of the Students" in the Napoleonic wars. But to return to the illustrations of his monographs, Haeckel's easy hand at drawing made him improve upon nature and put more into the illustrations than he saw. His medusae assumed romantic movements. One new species he called *Mitrocoma annasethe* (the nightbonnet of Anna Sethe, his wife) because the tentacles flowing from the umbrella reminded him of his wife's hair bursting out of her bonnet. The drawing shows the tentacles in such a way as to fit this comparison. Similarly Haeckel's radiolaria were too perfect all over. One had the impression that he first made a sketch from nature and then drew an ideal picture as he saw it in his mind.

Haeckel's genius, with all its different facets, came out first when he wrote his theoretical magnum opus under the influence of the *Origin of Species*, which started him on his career as Darwin's greatest apostle on the continent. The two volumes of the *Generelle Morphologie* established the basis of evolutionary thinking in morphology. The work pried into the workings of evolution in establishing the forms of animals. It put into the center the law of recapitulation, which Haeckel called the *biogenetisches Grundgesetz*, and tried to work out a phylogeny of form based upon this law. The importance of the work for the subsequent development of evolutionary morphology becomes evident if we mention only a few of the terms he introduced: ontogeny, phylogeny, gastrula, blastula, morula, protista. It established many of the ideas on growth, form, symmetry, and such basic elements of morphology, and many of these ideas as well as the new terms have been incorporated into elementary zoology. But with this great effort and the already mentioned monographs, to which later the big volume on the radiolaria of the "Challenger" Expedition were added, Haeckel's original contributions to zoology end, except for a long work on systematic phylogeny, the value of which is doubtful. From then on he was only the unflinching, fanatic apostle of evolution as he saw it and of the philosophy of monism, which he considered to be the logical consequence of Darwinism. This role he assumed and established in his two major popular books, the *Natural History of Creation* and *Anthropogeny.*

The present generation can hardly understand the influence Haeckel exercised through these books upon the minds of youth, of laymen in general, and also upon large sections of the professional world. Perhaps I may describe it best by my own experience. When I was a high school boy of about sixteen, I found myself in a period of doubt and revolution against traditional religion, a condition which was rather typical for the educated youth at that time. While in this stage, I got hold of some literature (paralleled somewhat in this country by Ingersoll's writings) which violently attacked traditions and commended an extreme materialistic philosophy. My father was a member of a citizens' club which owned a very large library, run as a lending library for the members. Once a week or so, I was sent there to exchange my parents' books, which meant that I went to the stacks to pick out what my parents wanted. The books were then presented to the librarian for registration. Of course, once in the stacks, I began to browse and to look for books which might satisfy my interests, and thus I struck the revolutionary books by Karl Vogt and the wild *Energy and Matter* of Büchner, a kind of atheistic Bible. As I could not dare to bring home such books openly, I hid them under my coat, read them secretly, and returned them to the shelves the same way, some weeks later. In this way I found Haeckel's history of creation one day and read it with burning eyes and soul. It seemed that all problems of heaven and earth were solved simply and convincingly; there was an answer to every question which troubled the young mind. Evolution was the key to everything and could replace all the beliefs and creeds which one was discarding. There were no creation, no God, no heaven and hell, only evolution and the wonderful law of recapitulation which demonstrated the fact of evolution to the most stubborn believer in creation. I was so fascinated and shaken up that I had to communicate to others my new knowledge, and this was done in the school yard, on school picnics, and among friends. I remember vividly a scene during a school picnic when I stood surrounded by a group of schoolboys to whom I expounded the gospel of Darwinism as Haeckel saw it. Another boy, who was already destined to become a parson like his father, passed and remarked, "He is again at converting." Indeed my zeal, which was Haeckel's zeal, was that of a missionary. I might be excused because of my age, but Haeckel never ceased to be a fanatic, bigoted zealot for his philosophy

[35]

of monism. It was at that time that I gave my first talk on evolution (of course a dramatic digest of Haeckel) before a boys' club. I wish I had a copy of this performance.

There is no doubt that hundreds of thousands, young and old, inside and outside Germany, were impressed in the same way, and that thus Haeckel became one of the most beloved and most hated men of his time. For many years he must have spent most of his working hours writing polemic pamphlets against his critics, and some of these are quite amazing. He produced only one more scientific book, as has already been mentioned, a systematic phylogeny in which he tried to develop his somewhat naive type of evolutionary trees for the whole living world, freely inventing ancestral groups where he needed them.

Real trouble was in store for him when he once more returned to a popular presentation of his monistic evolutionary philosophy in his book *The Riddle of the Universe.* Compared with this, his previous books were only mild statements. In an aggressive, fanatic spirit he presented his solutions for all riddles of matter and mind, bridging difficulties with bland assertions. Even his friends were shocked by the superficiality of his arguments and the sloppy handling of the facts. A real storm brewed when he was accused of having falsified pictures of embryos which were to prove the absence of differences in animal and human development. There was no doubt that the originals had been tampered with in the reproduction, though an exact copy would have been just as good for illustrating his argument. It may be considered as certain that Haeckel did not intend any falsification for which there was no reason. He had simply indulged in his old tendency to conventionalize his drawings and to make them approach an ideal picture he had in his mind. This is, of course, not an excuse for a naturalist, who should reproduce nature faithfully. There was a great outcry from philosophers and theologians, joined also by some of his colleagues, demanding Haeckel's removal from his chair with the Socratic indictment of corruptor of youth. But the protector of Jena University, the Grand Duke of Saxe-Weimar, proud of the enlightened tradition of his family and personally friendly to Haeckel, refused to interfere with the professor's right to his opinions and his responsibility for his writings. After all, Haeckel and his house in Jena had become a kind of European institution.

When I first met Haeckel he was already a septuagenarian. When Richard Hertwig brought him to my room I knew at once, from the many pictures I had seen, who the visitor was. His was a most conspicuous and impressive appearance. He must have been six and a half feet tall, with an erect, athletic body. On his shoulders sat an unusually large head, with a broad, high-arched forehead, surrounded by a white mane which continued into a long white beard. He wore the usual professor's wide-brimmed fedora which for him had to be made to order, since no store kept such a large hat size. Seeing him with his hat on, one thought at once of the Teutonic god Wotan. But while that embattled god had one eye covered, Haeckel looked at you with sparkling, boyish eyes of the most brilliant sky-blue I ever saw. But then came the disappointment; when he started speaking he spoke in a high pitch, completely out of tune with the huge body. His temperament was immense, and he was constantly on the move. But what he said was rather disappointing. I was working at that time, almost fifty years ago, with the strange, partly neotenic larval forms of tropical *Amphi-oxus* species described as *Amphioxides* and had indulged in some (not so good) phylogenetic speculations. I showed Haeckel some slides, but his comments showed that his ideas were still those of the naive phylogeny of his youth.

The last time I saw Haeckel he was past eighty and in bad shape. He had broken his hip, and though it had healed he was condemned to an armchair in his house. He complained bitterly, as his still fiery temperament made it hard for him to keep quiet. In addition he had gone through some bitter disappointment. In his older days he had spent much time upon building and establishing a phyletic museum which a rich admirer, Ritter, had endowed. Here he wanted to exhibit evolution, as he saw it, as a kind of Darwinian shrine for freethinkers. When the time of his retirement came, his great wish was to have a successor who would build up this museum according to his ideas. His eyes fell upon Ludwig Plate, who had written a rather good book on Darwinism, was an all-around zoologist with experience in collecting abroad, and had begun to dabble with the genetics of mice. In spite of warnings against this notorious bully, Pan-Germanist, and racist, Haeckel insisted on making him his successor. It did not take long until Plate pushed Haeckel out of his museum, where he had still kept a room, and actually forbade him to enter the building. To make matters worse,

[38]

Plate formally accused Haeckel of having stolen books belonging to the university. Haeckel had given his private library to the museum, and it seems that when he was driven out he took some of what had been his own books to his house. On this Plate based his public accusation. I, myself, have read Haeckel's letters to Richard Hertwig, reporting on his misery. Hertwig, Haeckel's former student, wrote to his own former student, Plate, and asked him to behave better toward the grand old man, drawing his attention to the unanimous condemnation of his actions by all decent people. This letter I read also. But Plate refused to budge, and thus Haeckel's last years were very unhappy.

While I am mentioning the doings of this unpleasant character Plate, I cannot help inserting the story of a scene which I witnessed and which characterizes well the brutal type he represented. At a meeting of the zoological society Professor Plate had announced a paper on a remarkable elephant embryo. Before the meeting I was looking at some exhibits with Spemann when we were joined by Plate who offered to show us his elephant embryo. He produced a jar of about five by ten inches which contained a completely developed fetus the size of a newborn puppy, covered with dark hair, showing long claws on all toes, and having a proboscis-like protrusion one or two inches long at the head. Plate told us that he had been so lucky as to buy the precious specimen from an Arab near the Red Sea and then raved about the immense phylogenetic importance of the specimen, especially the hair and claws. Spemann took a good look and asked Plate what it meant that the embryo had only a single large median eye which in addition was located below the proboscis where the mouth should be. Spemann saw at once that the specimen was a cyclopean monster, a kind of freak which frequently has a single eye below the nose, which might grow out proboscis-like. The elephant embryo of the clever Arab was a cyclopean dog (or jackal) embryo. Did this silence Plate? Not at all. The next day he presented without wincing a paper on a cyclopean monster of a dog which might be mistaken for an elephant fetus!

Karl Gegenbaur
Aside: K. FISCHER

Another student of J. Müller, who attained to greatness and was for some years Haeckel's colleague in Jena, was Karl Gegenbaur. He also started with marine zoology, and his monograph on Mediterranean heteropods and pteropods is still a classic. The choice of this subject might indicate an esthetic leaning in his young days as there is nothing more strangely beautiful in the animal kingdom (perhaps excepting some nudibranchs) than these Mediterranean forms. When I was a young student I had the good luck to stay for a couple of months at the Russian Marine Laboratory located in Villefranche on the French Riviera. There was nothing fancy at this place. The Russians had bought an old prison located at the seashore and consisting mainly of a large hall plastered with stone slabs still holding the large, rusty iron rings to which the prisoners had been chained. Into this hall which served as aquarium a few cubicles with windows had been built, and these were the laboratories, library, and so forth. A director, the charming and jolly Davidoff, ran the place under the titular director Professor Korotneff in Kiev—when the latter appeared, the townspeople called him Monsieur Quarante-neuf. An old fisherman, Manjapan, and his son, Honoré, were the entire personnel. There was no instruction or assistance of any kind; one picked out what material one wanted and worked with it on one's own. For a young student, first confronted with one of the richest marine faunas, this was a bewildering and exciting task and probably not very different from the situation in which Gegenbaur and Haeckel found themselves when they first worked in this region. Villefranche had, and probably still has, wonderful plankton. When one arrived at the institute in the morning, the fisherman had already returned from the morning's haul. In the entrance hall on a stone table stood a series of large battery jars with the booty. When one approached them at first they seemed empty. Actually each one contained some of the completely transparent major members of the Mediterranean plankton fauna. The first sight of the large glasslike *Ctenophora* and *Siphonophora*, among them the unbelievable "belt of Venus," was overwhelming. But most impressive were the large, oddly shaped snails, the naked *Pterotrachea* and *Carinaria* with its tiny shell. First one saw nothing in the jar; then one noticed one or more pairs of big black eyes without a body belonging to them; and, when one had the proper angle, the glasslike body with the fantastic form was delineated. One ran to the library to find out what odd creatures these were, and there Gegen-

[41]

baur's monograph told the story, and one came easily to the conclusion that forty years earlier one might also have chosen this group.

Gegenbaur himself, like his friend Haeckel, soon came under the spell of the rising Darwinian doctrine, and he started his life's work in the comparative anatomy of vertebrates. Comparative anatomy had already had a great past since Cuvier's time. But it became a real science only when evolution gave the comparison a real meaning—similarity by descent. It was Gegenbaur more than anybody else who laid the foundations of comparative anatomy as a study in evolution. His work on the extremities (the archipterygium theory), the branchial arches of the head skeleton, the segmentation of the head and the head nerves opened up an immense field of study and laid down the classic methods of comparison.

In his work Gegenbaur was just the opposite of Haeckel. He clung strictly to the facts and insisted on the minutest details. This does not mean that he lacked imagination. His theories of the evolution of limbs and the cranial skeleton were daring hypotheses which evoked wide discussion and set the pace for the evolutionary phase of comparative anatomy. But in developing hypotheses he studied the factual material as thoroughly as possible and worked as a real anatomist. As a professor of human anatomy for the major part of his life in Heidelberg, he was naturally acquainted with the minutest details of structure, and thus he remained also a dissecting anatomist when he went into the wider field of comparative anatomy. Human anatomy meant to him understanding the details of structure of man by their evolution, and comparative anatomy became the method of understanding evolution of form. In time Gegenbaur was reproached with neglecting development and physiological function. But at the time he did his main work, in the decades after Darwin, the limitation of the scope of his work was his greatness. It led to the fascinating development of comparative anatomy which continued with his students Fürbringer and Göppert down almost to the present time in the person and the work of the great Russian scholar, Severtzoff (with whom I could repeatedly discuss the meaning of comparative anatomy and embryology in regard to evolution).

In later years Gegenbaur put the facts and his way of looking at them into two voluminous textbooks, which for decades were used by thousands of students. His human anatomy tried to mitigate the dullness of descriptive anatomy by introducing at every point comparison with the vertebrate ancestors. But it was still a very difficult book for the average student, and I do not think that it could be a great success nowadays, apart from the change of emphasis upon topographical and functional anatomy. His huge volume on comparative anatomy was still more difficult reading and of use only to the specialist. But it characterizes the type of comparative anatomy which Gegenbaur introduced and is a landmark in the history of biology.

When I came to Heidelberg in 1896 as a premedical student, Gegenbaur, though a septuagenarian, was still professor of anatomy and gave the major daily lecture on human anatomy as well as the dissecting course. Thus I was able to be his student for two years. When I first entered his office to secure his signature for my study list, and every time afterward, I was impressed by his presence, which might be called majestic. He was very tall, heavy, and erect, and moved slowly. His face was parchment-like with deep wrinkles and adorned with a white goatee, and dark, penetrating eyes were overshadowed by a noble forehead. There was something forbidding in his appearance, and the young student felt awed and very small. He did not smile—and in two years I never saw him smile—but looked sternly at his visitor. I do not know whether I appeared to him to be one of those students bent on having a good time who chose Heidelberg as an appropriate place for wasting the first year of academic freedom. Instead of simply signing my book, as customary, he gave me a kind of scolding, meant as a friendly exhortation but coming out like a dressing down. He said that there were many different distractions for a student but that he had no use for anybody who did not work hard and regularly and that he would not stand any abuse of academic freedom. And he meant what he said. When a student was absent from the daily dissecting class for a few days, Gegenbaur simply had the leg or arm or whatever it was he was working on removed and the table assigned to another student. The number of students was, of course, small, so actually he knew everyone and the quality of his work, since he visited daily with every single student, checking upon his progress and convincing himself that he understood what he was dissecting. These visits were much dreaded, for nothing escaped his watchful eyes. I once had to dissect the muscles of the calf, and it was prescribed that the gastrocnemius had to be completely cleaned and isolated without cutting its heads and the deeper muscles worked out with the gastrocnemius intact. I did not succeed in this and severed one of the heads of this muscle in order to dig beneath it. Gegenbaur came and at once growled, "What did you do here?" I stuttered, "I thought. . . ." "You did not think at all," Gegenbaur thundered while all the other students listened, and he gave me a sound scolding for messing up my material. But such was the aura of greatness that surrounded the professor that one did not feel insulted by his scorn. This strange hypnotism of a great personality came out best in his lectures. For some reason or other his voice did not carry any more, and one could hardly understand a word of what he said. There stood the old man in the center of the steep anatomical theater, next to him a skeleton on which he pointed out with a pair of forceps the area of insertion of a muscle or whatever he was lecturing about, and the students heard almost nothing but "Bang, bang, bang, here, here." One would have thought that the students would run away and not reappear. But everybody was in his seat daily and listened to this performance out of respect and reverence for the great master.

Not many had a chance to meet Gegenbaur outside the classroom. He took no part in the social affairs of the small but lively university, and he did not often have guests at his house, though students in those days were frequently invited to dinner in a professor's house. I never paid the formal visit at his home which was the preliminary to an invitation. But any number of stories went around about the dullness of his parties where his remote matter-of-factness made a light or spirited conversation difficult. A typical conversation at dinner in his house was described thus: The house was located near a railway track, which at that time cut right through the loveliest residential section in town. For a long time nobody spoke. Then Gegenbaur said, "A train is just passing by." Fifteen minutes of silence, after which Gegenbaur said, "Another train is just passing." Another very characteristic story is this. Gegenbaur had a not too young daughter, and the mother was most anxious to attract a potential suitor. One such was invited for dinner, and Mrs. Gegenbaur tried to start a conversation by saying, "Mr. X looks so much younger than he is." The daughter caught the ball and retorted that she thought he looked much older. But before the ladies could spin a conversation around this theme Gegenbaur barked, "Nonsense, he looks exactly as old as he is."

Nevertheless there must have been another side to Gegenbaur's nature, from which we youngsters were excluded. This can be gathered from the fact of his friendship with the glittering, vain philosopher Kuno Fischer, at that time one of the most discussed figures of Heidelberg University. He was a brilliant historian of philosophy and a famous lecturer with a good deal of the ham actor in him. The stories about his vanity were legion, but nobody missed his famous lectures, especially one course on Goethe's *Faust* in which he recited the entire drama by heart, apparently incidentally, but with well-prepared intention, acting like a professional actor and enjoying the students' applause. Whenever there was a chance for hamming he did not miss it. I once witnessed the following scene. There was no co-education at that time in Heidelberg, and female students (mostly Russians), admitted hesitatingly by only a few professors, were a rare sight. Thus Kuno Fischer's lectures were attended only by men. One day a lady appeared and sat at the end of a bench next to the aisle through which the professor had to enter from the rear of the hall. When he arrived and saw the girl, he planted himself in front of her in a dramatic pose, stared at her for a long time with an expression of horror, and finally exclaimed in the dramatic accents of a perfect ham actor, "A lady!! In *my* lecture!!!" The poor girl ran away under the frenetic applause of the not very chivalrous students. Two years later Heidelberg opened the gates to coeds and Kuno Fischer had to give his lectures in the auditorium because of the crowds of women registered. I cannot leave Kuno Fischer without telling a little story which *se non è vero è ben trovato*. The philosopher had been elevated by the Grand Duke of Baden, one of his admirers, to the rank of excellency. Soon afterward, a student came and said to the professor, "Will Your Excellency excuse if I ask the favor of Your Excellency whether Your Excellency. . . ." Kuno Fischer interrupted and said, "Please, not all the time, only here and there."

This, then, was the very unlike friend of Gegenbaur. On Saturday afternoons one could see two old gentlemen slowly climbing the famous hill road to the Heidelberg

Castle: one, short, stocky, clean shaven, with a strangely bent nose; the other, tall, erect, lordly looking, with a white beard. Every twenty steps or so they would stop, face each other, and discuss vividly, resuming their walk after a few minutes. The strangely matched pair, Karl Gegenbaur and Kuno Fischer, must have had some important intellectual bonds across the difference of their personalities. But nobody ever knew what they were discussing in view of one of the most charming landscapes in the world.

3

Founding Fathers of Classical Zoology

Frankfurt am main, my home town, was still a free city when my great teacher, Otto Bütschli, grew up there. This meant a city republic with a thousand-year-old tradition of self-government and corresponding civic pride. Frankfurters considered themselves a special breed and were inordinately proud of their achievements. The city was a rich and well-built one which helped its own cultural institutions to develop to such a level that, a generation or two later, they could be incorporated directly into a modern university. Since Bütschli and I grew up in the same atmosphere, my own experiences may be used as background for his early days.

Otto Bütschli

Asides: H. REICHENBACH, E. WASMANN, K. VON ZITTEL,
E. STRASBURGER, C. WALDEYER, C. AND F. WINTER,
L. ASKENASY, W. ROUX, H. DRIESCH, C. HERBST,
J. J. VON UEXKÜLL, H. SPEMANN

When I chose Heidelberg as my first university, the main reason was that I wanted to become a student of Otto Bütschli. Though the wishes of my parents made me enroll as a premedical student, I hoped to switch over to zoology at the first good occasion, and therefore the professor of zoology was for me the center of attraction. I was well acquainted with the merits of the different schools from the already mentioned evening lectures of H. Reichenbach which I had attended for three years while still in high school. This remarkable high school teacher lectured for the local natural history society, named after a collector and founder of the museum, Senckenberg, which had for many years been an intellectual power in Frankfurt.

These courses given for the Senckenberg Society, attended by physicians, school teachers, and amateur zoologists, were the most stimulating ones I ever attended. Reichenbach had renounced the career of a research zoologist in order to make a living as a school teacher, but he kept the research spirit alive. He followed the literature closely—the society had a splendid library—and took sides violently in the discussions of the day. As he was not bound to any program or curriculum in his lectures, he made them more of a spirited discussion of the problems which agitated biological science than a systematic survey of a detailed field. Thus embryology and microscopic anatomy, taxonomy and ecology, general physiology and animal psychology were discussed in a personal and exciting way. For each of these discussions he brought the great publications of the past, monographs, special papers, and all the classics of three or four centuries; and after the lecture one could thumb through Malpighi, Rösel von Rosenhof, Spallanzani, Vesalius, and all the others in original editions, certainly a great experience for a young beginner. The lectures became especially dramatic when one of Reichenbach's favorite subjects was approached. He had done some work on ants, and thus he became a violent partisan in the discussion raging at that time of whether ants are reflex automatons or are endowed with psychic qualities. The physiologist Bethe had started the extreme view of reflex automatons and had performed a large set of experiments to prove his point, experiments which were later shown to be based upon insufficient knowledge of the material. His most powerful adversary was the Jesuit Father Wasmann, an uncontested authority on ants who disposed of Bethe's claims by brilliant experiments and observations. Reichenbach presented all this in a dramatic way accentuated by the use of expressive local dialect words. Thus his lectures gave much more than formal university courses could have given, and I am grateful to this day to that man of real scientific spirit and intellectual honesty, shining beneath the shell of a queer, red-nosed, faunlike old bachelor with a golden heart and razor-sharp wit.

As I have promised not to present formal biographies but rather to paint sketches in a more or less rambling way, the mention of Father Wasmann, S.J., may justify a short aside. There are probably not many left who knew him, though his memory is still vivid, especially in Catholic circles, and a biological periodical published by the University of San Francisco bears the name *Wasmannia*. At a much later period of my life I had frequent occasions to meet with this remarkable man, who was certainly the greatest expert on ants, myrmecophiles, and termitophiles of his time. But what made him most conspicuous was his acceptance of evolution as a scientific fact. At that time the church still opposed evolution, which it accepted only much later with the exception, of course, of the human soul. Thus Wasmann was in a very difficult and exposed position among his own people. He was certainly cautious when it came to discussing man, and here he kept within the limits expected from a Jesuit priest, but otherwise he stated his dangerous views quite openly on many occasions.

Personally he was a very fine type. He came from a good Hamburg family; his appearance was refined and sensitive, and his face, rather transparent from lung trouble, beautifully modeled; and his quiet aristocratic manners made him conspicuous in any group. Though retiring and unassuming he was clearly conscious of his ability and worth and spoke with authority and self-reliance. He was in no way unworldly and enjoyed good company and a gay conversation over a glass of champagne. Nevertheless, in talking and discussing with him one had the feeling that in the depth of his mind was hidden something which one

[52]

could not fathom. Did he have inner conflicts on account of the artificial limit he had to set for evolution? Did he have conflicts with his superiors, or both? I once got a hint when I met at a diplomatic function one of the top men of the Jesuit hierarchy, a very impressive old gentleman. Naturally the conversation turned to Wasmann, whom he greatly admired. But he added, somewhat enigmatically, "We do not object to anything he thinks; but he should be more careful with what he writes."

To return again to Frankfurt in the nineties, Reichenbach frequently pointed to the work of Bütschli, whom he described not only as a great zoologist but as a son of our town (like his contemporaries A. Weismann and C. Chun), who had received much of his scientific education right there in the Senckenberg Society. Reichenbach also brought Bütschli's classic monograph on cell division, which had been published by the same society in 1876, and thus Bütschli became my choice for a teacher. When I presented myself for registration the first thing after my arrival in Heidelberg, he did not lecture me as Gegenbaur did but inquired in the friendly manner of a compatriot about my family, which was not unknown to him. Thus he captivated me at once as a person and prepared the way for the relationship of student to master, later to become one of real friendship. Though I could not yet enter the laboratory as a full-fledged member of the scientific family since I was a premedical student, Bütschli quickly realized that I was in earnest and permitted me to come to the laboratory in my free hours and occupy myself with small voluntary chores like stretching butterflies for the collection or drawing the legend and explanation for a dissection. Thus I entered the spirit of the group and became attached to the master before I was ready to become one of his special students.

I have twice published a rather complete biographical sketch of Otto Bütschli and therefore do not want to repeat myself. Thus I shall give here only the skeleton of such a serious memoir and indulge more in reminiscing of the small events of daily life which, after all, make up the life of a great man just as they do that of a less great one. When I came to Heidelberg the professor was forty-eight years old and already had behind him the major part of the work upon which his fame was based. Since I had been raised in the same town he frequently talked with me about his younger days, and I learned much of his early development. His family had come to Frankfurt a few generations earlier from Switzerland, as the name also indicated. According to the conceited ways of the natives of Frankfurt he was therefore an "intruder" or "shifter," as only those who could trace their ancestry in the town for a few hundred years were considered real Frankfurters. Strangely enough Bütschli did not graduate from the humanistic Gymnasium, which alone, at that time, prepared for the university, but from the new-fangled *Musterschule*, which offered no Greek but English instead and more science. This is probably the reason why he started his study in chemistry and mineralogy at the Institute of Technology in Karlsruhe. He later chose mineralogy as his major and took his doctor's degree in Heidelberg with a thesis in mineralogy, and chemistry and zoology as minors. For a year or two he served as an assistant to the young professor of

Franz Leydig, 1903

Ernst Haeckel in Penang, ca. 1898 (Photograph by Hüttenbach)

From left to right, standing: Koltzoff, Manjapan; seated, middle row: Redikorzew, Davidoff, Hartmann, Davidoff's mother, Goldschmidt; in front: fisherman's boys. Villefranche, 1899

Otto Bütschli, 1908

geology and mineralogy at the Karlsruhe Institute of Technology, Karl von Zittel, who was later to become the great paleontologist.

I do not remember hearing Bütschli speak about his first boss. But it so happened that thirty years later I was one of Zittel's students in Munich, and so I shall switch the scene for a moment to Munich, a generation later. At that time Zittel was already a famous man, one of the greatest paleontologists, a very influential member of the university, and, if I am not mistaken, President of the Royal Academy, whose members appeared at formal sessions in knee breeches, gold-embroidered frock coat, cocked hat, and sword. Some of them, like the giant Göbel, the botanist, made a great showing in this outfit, but less well-built ones were a different sight. Zittel was a very serious and dignified-looking man with a short, black beard. He lectured one term on general geology for a big class, and this was a brilliant, unforgettable course. The other term he taught paleontology for a small group of students. We sat around a long table, the professor in the center. He brought to each lecture hundreds of fossil specimens taken from the wonderful Bavarian state collection, which was destroyed by bombs and fire in the recent war. The lecture itself was very dull because he overcrowded it with names of innumerable species. Many of these he passed around, but, until the specimen reached you, you did not know what it was to show. Nevertheless, it was, of course, a great experience to handle a selected group of perfect fossil specimens from all over the animal kingdom. I tried to learn more by registering for a laboratory course in paleontology, but this was a failure because, I think, of Zittel's strange pedagogic methods. When I came for the first class it turned out that I was the only student. Zittel gave me a table in a window niche of one of the halls of the museum, which was unheated (it was a winter term). Then he brought me a box of assorted fossil Foraminifera and two French monographs and asked me to determine and draw a number of species. This I did every day for a week. Finally Zittel returned, looked at my drawings and the names I had found for the specimens, and said, "You may determine some more." Thus I sat another week freezing in the cheerless room, all by myself, until Zittel returned again, looked at my specimens, and said, "You may determine a few more; they are very interesting *Leitfossilien*." But when this scene repeated itself after the third week I quit, and thus I do not know to the present day whether Zittel intended to teach me anything else. He probably was not interested in a mere zoology student, since all his real students were primarily geologists.

Thus we return to Bütschli, who, while an assistant to Zittel, decided to quit mineralogy and become a zoologist. He went first to Leipzig, where Leuckart was a famous teacher. But for some reason he hated the atmosphere of this famous laboratory and did not like the professor, either. In addition, he felt unhappy in the ugly Saxon town. Then came the Franco-Prussian War, and he had to serve as a reserve officer. His duties, however, left him time to write, at the front, one of his first cytological papers, on spermatogenesis. It is signed O. B., Lieutenant in Reserve in this and that regiment. Lest somebody think that this marks Bütschli as a Prussian militarist, it should be said that he was one of the few Germans in similar positions at that time who was not what the Germans call *militärfromm*. After the successful war the love for the military so increased in Germany that finally a man was without social standing if he was not an officer in reserve. Even in the universities one found professors who were prouder of their status as lieutenant second grade in reserve than of their membership in a great faculty. My later superior in Heidelberg, Professor A. Schuberg, sported visiting cards—at that time an important and much used part of social equipment—which read, Schuberg (without a Christian name, in the affected style of the officer corps), Second Lieutenant in Reserve in this or that regiment, and, below this, Professor of Zoology at the University of Heidelberg. On Emperor Wilhelm's birthday, all these men donned their uniforms and strutted around the main street. There one could see, in my time, the Falstaff-shaped chemist Curtius in the tight-fitting uniform of a lieutenant of the hussars, an utterly ridiculous sight, and many others like him making fools of themselves. I am sure that nobody saw Bütschli in a uniform after the end of the war.

At that time, 1871, he went for two years to Kiel as an assistant to the pedantic taxonomist Möbius. He never mentioned these years, though he did basic work there on free-living nematodes which was to become decisive for him. In the study of these transparent creatures he noticed their sex cells, which allowed observation of a good deal of the process of fertilization in the living egg, and he was the first to see here the entrance of the sperm into the egg and some of its subsequent fate. This set his mind upon the study of cell division and fertilization, and, as this was a subject of no interest to his surroundings, he decided to return to his home town, Frankfurt, and work there as a gentleman scholar away from any university laboratory and completely upon his own. He liked, in addition, the cultural atmosphere of Frankfurt, where he had many friends and participated in many activities. I know that he belonged to a small circle of young men interested in belles-lettres to which one of my uncles also belonged. During these years he did an immense amount of work which he first communicated shortly in 1875, followed by a big monograph in 1876. These were his studies on the division of the cell, fertilization, and the conjugation of infusoria, which made him one of the founding fathers of cytology.

It is difficult to understand why this monograph, which was published in the quarto volumes of the Senckenberg Society and had a tremendous effect upon the development of cytology and protozoology, has been largely forgotten. It contains an unusual series of basic discoveries presented with minute care and, moreover, from a high philosophical level. It gave the first correct description of mitotic division in different objects, with emphasis on the happenings in the cytoplasm, and the first attempt at a physiochemical explanation. It presented the discovery of the fertilization cone, the first stages of the entrance of the sperm into the egg, and the proof that only one sperm enters. It proved for the first time that the polar bodies are real cells, the products of an unequal but typical cell division. It gave the entire sequence of events from the entry of the sperm to the first cleavage, though missing the union of the nuclei which was inferred but not observed. It contained the proof that infusoria are unicellular animals; that what had been described as sperm bundles were mitotically dividing micronuclei; that conjugation is a mutual fertilization involving a definite behavior of the micronuclei; that the new macronucleus is derived from the fertilization nucleus. In addition to these factual discoveries Bütschli concluded that protozoa always divide mitotically and that conjugation must involve a rejuvenation. In 1875 he started breeding infusoria under control and mixed cultures of different provenience hoping to find physiological differences leading to conjugation, and he constructed physical models in explanation of cell division by surface forces.

The greatest gaps in this work were, as already mentioned, the fate of the sperm nucleus after entering the egg, a gap which at the same time was filled by O. Hertwig, studying the more favorable sea urchin egg; and, of course, the role and behavior of the chromosomes in mitosis, which were discovered years later by Flemming after the introduction of staining techniques not yet available to Bütschli. The shift of emphasis onto the chromosomes, especially after Van Beneden's discovery of the number rule in the early eighties, pushed the former discoveries into the background. Another reason for the neglect of Bütschli's work was the prominent role in his studies of the infusoria, animals which were of little interest to the anatomists and histologists who took over the early cytological work. Furthermore, Bütschli did not continue his cytological work

[59]

because he became fascinated by the physiology of protoplasm, which led him to the protozoa as a suitable material
for such work. Finally the intensity of Strasburger's attack upon the problems of cell division in plants drew attention more upon the work of the great plant cytologist, who
had started his work in Bonn more or less simultaneously.
Bütschli told me—and in view of his character there can
be no doubt of the truth of his words—that at first Strasburger could not interpret his slides of dividing plant cells.
At that time he learned that Bütschli was doing similar
things and visited him (Bonn and Frankfurt are not far
apart). Bütschli demonstrated his material and discussed
his interpretations, and this first opened Strasburger's
eyes. But, while Bütschli kept adding still more facts, Strasburger published his first report and continued through all
his life with cytological work, founding the greatest school
of plant cytology to which almost everybody belonged toward the end of the nineteenth century. I met Strasburger
only once and remember only his tall, slender figure and
good head, without the usual professorial beard and with
a very prominent nose. The conversation must have been
only small talk, for nothing has remained in my memory.
Perhaps I was also prejudiced and restrained on the basis
of the just reported happenings.

Bütschli himself resented very much in later years the
small regard for his work, though at the time it appeared
it earned him the professorship in Heidelberg while he was
still young, without any of the waiting in line I have described above, except two years as docent in Karlsruhe.
The high point of his resentment was reached, according

to his own confession, ten years later at the occasion of a jubilee in Heidelberg. The main speaker was the anatomist Waldeyer, who had made his fame by a classical study of the mammalian ovary. After this he did not do much original work but became a very powerful politician of science, much sought out as a brilliant orator and teacher of medical students. In my younger days there was hardly a festival occasion in science where Waldeyer was not conspicuously occupying the center of the stage, with his white beard flowing almost down to his belt. (This male secondary sex characteristic, some of his colleagues insinuated, was his major claim to fame.) In the early days of cytology, after 1880, he wrote regular reviews on the progress of this subject, and in one of them he had the happy idea of coining the word chromosome, though he had never worked with these structures. Thus he made the rise of cytology the topic of his jubilee talk in Heidelberg. One of the listeners was Bütschli, whose name was never mentioned.

It is interesting even today to look at the beautiful lithographic plates of Bütschli's memoir of 1876. He was highly gifted artistically, painted nice water colors, and frequently drew witty cartoons. In order to get the most lifelike reproduction of his figures he drew them himself directly upon the lithographic stone, helped by his friend Winter. I cannot mention this name without inserting a long overdue tribute to the Winter family, which was for decades a power in scientific illustration and a godsend to the zoologists of the world around the end of the nineteenth century and the beginning of the twentieth. Winter was a lithographer who had come from Switzerland to Frankfurt. He combined a supreme technical skill with artistic feeling and interest in the objects of nature and thus was led into the field of scientific illustration. Together with a businessman, Werner, who furnished the funds, he founded the lithography firm of Werner and Winter, which was soon to become the supreme leader of scientific illustration in the world. All zoologists of that time tried to have the lithographic plates accompanying their publications executed by Werner and Winter. I frequently visited the place, as young Winter, who was trained to succeed his father, was my friend. The famous shop was nothing but a few flats in an apartment house. Here were stacked the beautifully smooth Solenhofen limestone slabs which made the best lithographic stone. A few draftsmen, with the quiet, efficient Winter at their head, transferred the scientist's drawings to the stone after Winter had indicated where to improve the originals and where to follow them closely, discerning instinctively what was important and what due to insufficient draftsmanship. Through his friendship with many zoologists Winter acquired much special knowledge, but he realized that this did not suffice and had his son Fritz trained as a zoologist. Fritz took his doctor's degree with a protozoological thesis and later was a member of the "Valdivia" deep-sea expedition before he took over his father's work. The fine, superbly trained young man, husband and father, was to be one of the last victims of the First World War, just before the armistice. At this time began the slow but certain disappearance of scientific lithography, which could not compete any longer with photographic methods of illustration. Whether this is to be regretted or not, even today nobody can look, for example, at August Brauer's monograph on deep-sea fishes, with its plates drawn from nature and lithographed by Fritz Winter, without admiration for the exactness combined with beauty of these supreme examples of a kind of scientific illustration which has disappeared forever.

When I mention Bütschli's draftsmanship it comes to my mind how many of the old zoologists had this gift. I have already discussed Haeckel; I could add Carl Chun, the great marine zoologist, who adorned his house with frescoes; Boveri, who did oil paintings of merit; Doflein, the protozoologist, who was good at water colors; and many others. This ability can be understood as a part of the sense of form which makes a good naturalist and morphologist, and even today, when scientific illustration has become less important, many examples of the gift of draftsmanship will be found among zoologists. With Bütschli this was only a part of an all-around artistic nature which was revealed only to his friends. It was said that in his younger years he had had a beautiful singing voice, which he had ruined by chain-smoking cigars. When I knew him he still occasionally played the piano. In his spare time and during vacations he was a voracious reader of belles-lettres, and he was well acquainted with literature in many languages. Once he confided in me that he was occupied in translating Shakespeare's *Tempest*, one of his favorites, into German verse. The ease with which he produced rhymed skits for occasions in the laboratory suggests that he may have indulged secretly in verse writing.

[63]

When I became Bütschli's student he had been a professor for almost twenty years and had accomplished the major part of his zoological work. He had published the three volumes of his protozoology, involving a large amount of original work and checking upon the work of others. He had also published, apart from numerous studies in many fields of zoology, the work on the structure of protoplasm which was of all his work dearest to his heart. He had been attacked, vilified, and scorned but also praised highly for this presentation of the alveolar theory of the structure of protoplasm. Viewed in a historical perspective this was a great achievement, whatever the present-day ideas on the structure or absence of structure of protoplasm might be. It was not simply a description of structures as he saw them in the living and fixed cell but an attempt to understand the functions of protoplasm on a physical basis. One must not forget that at this time physical chemistry was just in its infancy, colloid chemistry did not yet exist, nothing was known of the structure of protein molecules, and enzyme systems had not yet entered biology. Thus Bütschli's attack upon the problem of protoplasm was not only novel but far ahead of his time. His artificial models of colloidal drops moving like amoebae meant an advanced program of the study of protoplasm rather than a playful occupation, as some of his less intelligent critics assumed. From the point of view of the historic advance of the theory of living matter, this work was indeed as important and far-reaching as its author was convinced that it was. The knowledge of the significance of his approach made him sensitive to the frequently malevolent attacks. There were professors who told their students that Bütschli's ideas were the result of watching his father making whipped cream in his confectionery shop. How Bütschli thought about his adversaries I could see in the marginal notes on his copies of his critics' papers. Such entries as "Ass!" and "Ignorance!" were rather on the mild side. I have noticed with pleasure that this was also the way Galileo dealt with his stupid critics.

It was only a few years after this period of Bütschli's work that I came to his laboratory. At that time he had completely left strictly zoological research. Convinced that the alveolar structure of protoplasm must have a broader meaning, he began the study of the structures of nonliving materials which he considered to be structurally related, i.e., everything which is now known as a colloid like gelatin and the colloidal silica compounds. He found everywhere the expected structures and thus furnished the rising science of colloid chemistry with a basic structural insight which this science always acknowledged gratefully, though the zoologists shook their heads at what had become of Bütschli. This was still more the case when he made pure chemical and mineralogical studies of inorganic products of the animal body, mollusc shells, calcareous and silica spicules, skeletons of sponges, and so forth. The following is evidence of his typical thoroughness and skill. In the calcareous spicules he found a completely new mineral and described it chemically and mineralogically. Chemists and mineralogists took up the subject later and were unable to find the new compound, which was thus considered to be the result of an erroneous analysis. Only a few years ago,

I received a paper by some American mineralogists who had, after fifty years, succeeded in repeating and confirming Bütschli's results and called the mineral (an unexpected salt of calcium) Bütschliite.

When Bütschli did this work on structures, he had the idea of convincing disbelievers by photographic records. I think this was the first time that morphological work was illustrated to a large extent by microphotographs (not photomicrographs, which is a distortion of the original meaning, namely, photographs taken through the microscope!). Out of his own slender pocket Bütschli paid a funny little photographer who hurried around the institute like a ghost and helped him with the technique which at that time was still in its beginning. But again Bütschli's critics reproached him for publishing photographs "which do not show anything, compared with a good drawing."

One might think that his neglect of genuine zoology made Bütschli a less good teacher. Actually he was a brilliant and fascinating teacher. He was more or less a zoological autodidact, and he told me frankly that in his first years as professor he was still deficient in some fields of zoology which he had to teach in the "big" lecture. Thus he dissected his first starfish ten minutes before he had to lecture on the subject. But when I knew him he was in complete mastery of all parts of zoology. Lecturing was not effortless for him. He could not speak easily and without preparation. He knew this and had stage fright before each lecture, and he was actually sick for two weeks before the start of a new term. He invariably spent a couple of hours each night in preparing his morning lecture. The students would not be aware of this as he delivered a brilliant lecture without notes, perfectly balanced and audible at every seat. But one noticed his nervous strain and also the strain on his voice and the tensity of his effort. With his facile hand he drew on the blackboard in many colors perfect pictures and diagrams, all of them of his own invention, conventionalized so as to cling to the memory of the student. Today, after almost sixty years, I could still draw many of them from memory. But he was greatest as teacher in the professional laboratory, as I have described him above.

The special students also had a chance to meet their worshiped master outside the institute. There was not much social life in his house, partly because his second marriage —after the death in childbed of his beloved first wife—was not too successful. But he liked one or another student to join him in the Saturday afternoon hike he took with his friend, the botanist Askenasy. This man was the prototype of the German professor of the comics: tall, thin, shortsighted, stooped, leaving his hat, coat, or umbrella in all kinds of places, and a confirmed bachelor, too. But he was an immensely cultured man, well read in almost anything. While walking through the lovely beechwoods covering the mountains next to town, the two scholars discussed almost everything; Bütschli, agitated, nervous, aggressive; Askenasy, timid, slow, but stubborn and full of information. The student coming along, often myself, of course kept his mouth shut while acquiring more than a liberal education. The hike always ended in one of the pleasant coffee gardens, where the conversation continued for hours over coffee and cake. Occasionally such hikes were made with the entire laboratory, to everybody's enjoyment. Years later, I was pleasantly reminded of these afternoons when Heidelberg University surprised me with a traveling fellowship which Askenasy had endowed in his will. Bütschli had proposed me as the first recipient in memory of those former associations.

During these years of 1896–1902, Bütschli, without wanting to, got into a fight which was based upon an important development in our science. In the nineties the science of experimental embryology had started its brilliant ascendancy. W. Roux had been the pioneer, but he soon stopped experimental work and became satisfied with theoretical discussions. The real leader was then Hans Driesch with his alter ego Curt Herbst. These two friends were men of independent means and kept away from the universities, doing their work at the Naples station and traveling in between. Driesch and also Herbst performed their famous experiments with the sea urchin egg, hydroids, and tunicates, and Driesch especially carried the causal analysis to unexpected depth. Today, when this type of experimental embryology is the common knowledge of all biologists, we realize the immense contribution of Driesch, who stands out as a great experimenter and deep thinker, far ahead of his time. Some of his early work done in the days before much was known of chromosomes, not to mention heredity and biochemistry, is still as significant as it was sixty years ago. In recent years Driesch's contribution seemed to have been eclipsed by the popular appeal of Spemann's great work, but I think there can be no doubt that Driesch was by far the greater analytical thinker and independent mind and in addition a pioneer of audacious experiments and ideas, while Spemann's greatness was his single-minded, even somewhat narrow, application to one task, pushed forward almost to perfection. But at the time Driesch's work was done he made the zoological profession his enemies by the overt conceit and overbearing attitude he exhibited both in his writings and in personal contacts. He left no doubt that he considered all other zoological work second rate, that he despised all evolutionary theory or comparative morphology. His was the only permissible causal attack upon biological problems. He snubbed everybody, kept away from university science, and even illustrated his papers with crude, ill-executed sketches, just to show that morphology did not mean anything for a real thinker. To make matters worse he drifted into his much-discussed neovitalism, reintroduced the Aristotelian entelechy, and produced his arrogant so-called first, second, and so forth proofs for vitalism. Thus, in spite of the brilliance of his work, he had more enemies than friends, and his personality was not very attractive, either. He carried a large, round head deep-set on his shoulders, and his sallow face reminded one of a tadpole. One always had the impression, when talking to him, that he considered it a great gift to the interlocutor that he stooped to speak.

Before 1900, Driesch and Herbst decided to settle in Heidelberg. Driesch was to be married, and he wanted Herbst to become a *Privatdocent* in order to conquer the universities for his ideas. Herbst did become *Privatdocent*

[69]

in Heidelberg, and, when Driesch later moved away—he left zoology and became professor of philosophy in Leipzig—Herbst changed considerably and grew beyond his former conceit and contempt for everybody but Driesch and his followers. He developed into a very fine person, in addition to remaining a great experimenter, and in 1920 succeeded Bütschli in the chair of zoology. When the Nazis came to power he showed the stuff he was made of. He never ceased denouncing them and made a point of visiting his Jewish friends when everybody could see it and of helping them to the last. Up to the last weeks of his life he wrote me letters which, had they been opened by the Gestapo, would have sealed his fate.

But to return to the nineties in Heidelberg. Driesch at once assembled around him a few men who shared his enthusiasm for vitalism and believed themselves to be a superior brand of scientists. The chief members of this little mutual admiration club were the eccentric mystic and physiologist Count von Uexküll, a very remarkable personality and a lifelong producer of a mixture of good science and mysticism or metaphysics; the later famous physiologist Magnus; and the chemical physiologist O. Cohnheim (who subsequently changed his name to Kästner). At scientific meetings they helped each other in the discussion and formed a rather aggressive group which succeeded in impressing many colleagues. I remember a meeting of the local naturalists' society in which Driesch read a paper on some of his experiments. While discussing environment and organism he wrote their relationship on the blackboard in the form of a mathematical function. This immensely impressed the young physicists and chemists with the new biology, though it was nothing more than a semantic playing with pseudomathematical exactness.

Though Bütschli had a very open mind and was inclined to welcome new and progressive methods, he did not like the superciliousness of this group which was so different from his own simplicity and modesty. In addition he got into personal trouble with them. I recount this as Bütschli told it to me afterward. Uexküll, who had started as a self-taught gentleman scholar, wanted to have a doctor's degree and approached Bütschli. He pointed to his many publications and hinted at his expectation of being given the degree without bothering much with the requirements. I suppose that Bütschli was already prejudiced because of the attitude of this group; in addition he was not fond of counts, and especially if they considered themselves entitled to special treatment. Thus Uexküll's demand for special consideration appeared to Bütschli as an insult, a kind of attempt to bribe himself into a degree. Bütschli actually blew his top and literally threw the Count out.

Nevertheless, the new propaganda for vitalism set Bütschli's philosophical mind in motion, and he began to study vitalistic literature and its philosophical background since antiquity. In some way which I do not remember, this led to an invitation to present one of the main addresses to the International Zoological Congress at Berlin, 1901, on the topic of "Mechanism and Vitalism." Bütschli at once started studying, comparing and analyzing the claims of both philosophies and checking upon his own mechanistic attitude. He took the preparation of this address very seriously and for more than a year did not think of much else. Whereas formerly, upon entering the laboratory he had sometimes assembled the students and asked them a tricky question in biochemistry, physiology, or any other outside field, he now came in shouting at one of us, "What do you think of this sentence of Kant?" Finally he saw clearly what he wanted to be his conclusion and finished an enlarged version of his address, which, I think, would still be good reading for aspiring biologists. For myself this brought an unexpected ordeal. A semipopular science magazine, *Die Umschau,* wanted to publish a shortened version of the address in time for the congress, and as Bütschli had no leisure to make this extract he asked me to do it instead. I was in no way prepared for a philosophical discussion—I was still a graduate student—but I could not decline the honor. Thus I sweated through many a hot Heidelberg summer night, trying to produce an abbreviated version without harm to the logic of the argument and not being certain that I understood everything. The product was accepted and printed under Bütschli's name; but I received the honorarium, which was better deserved than any other in my life.

While mentioning my own doings, I may describe also another comparable venture. Toward the end of the century appeared a book by Labbé in Paris on experimental cytology. This was the first attempt at assembling facts which were beginning to assume a major·importance. I was impressed with the book, and Bütschli suggested that I should translate it into German. He wrote to his publisher Engelmann, who declared his willingness to print it in a series edited by Wilhelm Roux. Thus I again spent my nights making this translation and finally was able to send it to the publisher. After some months the manuscript was returned with a letter from Roux, in which he said that this was indeed a very interesting book but that its value would be considerably enhanced if I would add a few notes which he, Roux, had written out for me. In the manuscript I found hundreds of notes in Roux's handwriting, some attached to practically every page, which uniformly ran about like this: "At this point it should be emphasized that Wilhelm Roux stated already in 1884 that . . ." and then followed some quotation which fitted or did not fit the occasion but glorified the father of *Entwicklungsmechanik*. I did not believe my eyes when I went through all these proposed "improvements." I could not accept this imposition and consulted with Bütschli, who did not spare strong language. But, as it was out of the question that a young student could hold out against a Roux and his pathological vanity, I wrote the publisher that I must regret, and the manuscript with Roux's additions ended in the wastepaper basket. If I had kept it, it would be a nice souvenir of the smallness of some great men.

I left Heidelberg in 1902 to make use of a better chance for an academic career, but I kept in touch with Bütschli not only by correspondence but in frequent meetings. He used to take his vacations in the Austrian Alps, where he would meet his friend, the excellent zoologist Eisig from Naples, for a few weeks of hiking in the mountains. The vacation usually wound up in Munich, where I would have a few days with my old teacher. During this period he suddenly changed his work back to genuine zoology. For years his students had urged him to write down and publish his brilliant lectures on comparative anatomy, as no readable book on this subject existed. Gegenbaur's big work was too detailed and dry. It is remarkable how many zoologists with a simultaneously analytical and imaginative mind had a weakness for comparative anatomy although they themselves did not work in the field. The reason is, clearly, that such topics as the comparative anatomy of the facial and visceral skeleton or of the urogenital system are not only models of logical clarity but simultaneously highly dramatic subjects. I know that not only Bütschli but also Boveri and Spemann loved to lecture on comparative anatomy and got mental satisfaction from it. Thus Bütschli decided to give in and to write such a book. What was at first a modest plan developed into a very ambitious one, a comparative anatomy of both invertebrates and vertebrates in a series of volumes. All illustrations were to be original, drawn after a unified plan by Bütschli and his devoted helpers, von Buddenbrock and Clara Hamburger. The first volume was finished and published, and the material and drawings were collected for much of the rest. Then the First World War interrupted the work. Bütschli, who had realized early what the end would be, suffered greatly mentally, and he suffered also bodily as he refused on principle to buy black-market food, without which nobody could sustain his strength. Thus his body became so weakened that the first bad cold after the war took him away. The book continued under an ill star. Bütschli's oldest student Blochmann, a good zoologist with the nature of an army sergeant, took it over to finish the work from Bütschli's ample notes, but he stalled indefinitely. Finally von Buddenbrock and Clara Hamburger took over and published some more installments which stretched over more than ten years. When the Nazis came to power they forbade any printing under C. Hamburger's name, and the whole work folded up, a torso.

Bütschli, who was a confirmed pessimist in spite of his open, simple nature, would not have expected anything better, but when I visited him last a few months before the end he was in unusually good spirits, though very thin and frail. He had great hopes for the future of Germany as a republic, since he had been always—a rarity among the conservative professors—a convinced republican. As a young man he had been active for the democratic party, even been on the stump before elections. This party, in Baden, was derived from the old republicans of 1848 and thus openly advocated a democratic republic. This was regarded as a personal insult by the old Grand Duke, a very popular and enlightened ruler, who was, ex officio, the rector of the university, the actual elected rector being called prorector. One can understand that the liberal monarch, who did everything in his power for the university, could not stomach anybody who wanted to do away with his throne, even in such an unfanatic and peaceful way as those democrats. Thus Bütschli became *persona non grata* at the Karlsruhe court. At that time a hierarchy of titles played a great role in the social life of the university. After a certain number of years a successful professor was made a *Hofrat*, later a *Geheimer Hofrat*, then a *Geheimer*

[75]

Rat, and a very few highly conspicuous ones finally *Exzellenz.* Bütschli was shown what the Grand Duke thought of democrats by being passed over when his time came so that he was always one or two promotions behind his contemporaries. He certainly was not interested in these titles, but both students and professors who did not know the reason wondered what was wrong with him. But when, after the lost First World War, Baden became a republic, one of the first actions of the democratic government was to bestow the title of excellency upon Bütschli, who in modesty enjoyed this vindication. I have met and known many great scholars and great personalities in all walks of life in the course of the years. Of all of them, Bütschli alone impressed me—and all his other students—as a genuine genius, completely apart from the merits of his work, which was great but not greater than that of other leaders and pioneers. It is difficult to put into words how a susceptible young person feels in his relations with a genius; it is a kind of worship, even of love, with an undertone of humility. Says Goethe (*Gespräche mit Eckermann,* 12. Mai 1825), "*Überall lernt man nur von dem, den man liebt.*"

The Brothers Hertwig
Asides: CROWNED ZOOLOGISTS, RUSSIAN GENTLEMEN AND SCHOLARS

When Haeckel was still a young professor in Jena, his best scholars were two medical students with a preference for zoology, the brothers Oscar and Richard Hertwig. Oscar was born in 1848, the same year as

Bütschli; Richard was two years younger, and both were destined to become great pioneers of modern zoology. They had grown up first in Thuringia, later in the small Hessian town of Friedberg, and they were supposed to take over the parental factory one day. But a high school teacher, obviously one of the fine type I have described above, recognized their gift for science and prevailed upon the father to allow his boys to study chemistry. The school teacher had been an admiring student of Haeckel and therefore persuaded the brothers to go to Jena, which would give them also a chance to hear Haeckel's lectures. But the professor of chemistry turned out to be so dull that the two students soon changed over to medicine, which also included zoology. Thus they came under Haeckel's influence at his best time, the late sixties, though they continued and finished their medical studies. During the Franco-Prussian War Oscar worked as a surgeon while Richard served as an orderly in a military hospital. Soon afterward Haeckel took them to the Mediterranean, actually to the beautiful shores of the Dalmatian coast and islands, and thus started them on their marine work, which for Richard meant first a thesis on the structure of the *Tunicata*. For many years thereafter the two brothers collaborated closely, and much of their famous work appeared under both names. This happy condition lasted until Richard received his first professorship of zoology in Königsberg, while Oscar, who took up a career in anatomy, remained in Jena.

In the early seventies the brothers went frequently to the seashore, bringing their own equipment, hiring a boat,

[77]

and living and working under the simplest conditions. Here they accomplished their first separate as well as common successes. The most far-reaching one was Oscar's work on the fertilization of the sea urchin egg, one of the great classics of our science. He was the first to follow the sperm nucleus to its union with the egg nucleus, and thus he solved the riddle of fertilization, which Bütschli had not succeeded fully in doing in his work of that time. It is not known why Richard did not collaborate in this great work, though there are hints that he was somehow connected with the observations.

As Oscar's later life was much less interesting and conspicuous than Richard's, we may first report on him. After the period of the common work, to be discussed below, Oscar did one more remarkable piece of work in which he established the cytological parallels between oogenesis and spermatogenesis. As an anatomist he drifted later more into embryology and histology, especially after he received a special professorship in Berlin for biological anatomy as opposed to medical human anatomy, which Waldeyer taught. His writings became more general, and he exercised a great influence through some of his books. The most important one was *The Cell and the Tissues*, in which he developed a biological and functional histology very different from the purely descriptive one usually taught. This book was a very brilliant performance and had a great influence upon histology at the end of the century, before the rise of modern cytology. His own work of that time, which was incorporated into the book, dealt with experiments on the cell, e.g., on segmentation under pressure and similar topics. But it did not lead to such brilliant results as the work of his younger days. He must have been an excellent teacher, as his textbook of embryology testifies. In the German original and in many translations this book taught a whole generation of students with a wonderfully clear presentation of the essentials. Later on, at the time when Richard became the greatest zoology teacher in Europe, not much was heard of Oscar, who was in not too good health. In advanced age he again started a new line of work on the effects of radiation upon the cell, partly in collaboration with his children Günther and Paula, both by then zoologists in their own right. Though he was the more brilliant of the two brothers— Richard always looked up to him even when he disagreed —and probably had been the greater force in their early common work, Oscar's influence and performance fell in time behind that of the younger brother. This may have been because of his completely different temperament. While Richard was an extrovert who retained his influence in science and community up to his eighty-seventh year, Oscar was remote, inaccessible, and not a friendly personality. He attracted, therefore, hardly any special students, H. Poll and his own children being almost the only ones of consequence. In his older days he developed that professorial egoism which was so frequently a consequence of the powerful position of the German university professor. I observed this when, in 1912, the later famous Kaiser Wilhelm Institute for Biology was being planned. Oscar tried to prevent this plan by all means, stating quite frankly that it would be insupportable for him if another person (who was to be Boveri) should work on comparable problems in the same town and with greater means than he had. (Actually at that time he did not do much research any more.) Then he proposed that instead of the great research institute a place for breeding laboratory animals should be founded. Fortunately such poor counsel did not prevail. This narrow attitude of an undoubtedly very great scholar made me little desirous of knowing more of him when I myself moved to Berlin, in spite of my friendship with his brother. Thus I can only report that in appearance he was small with a finely cut bald head, short gray beard, and a chilling expression in his extremely intelligent and keen face.

Richard Hertwig's career, after he took his medical degree in Bonn in 1872, started as *Privatdocent* under Max Schultze (who had given the first correct description of the cell). In 1875 he became docent in Jena, where his brother also worked, and in 1881 he received his first professorship in Königsberg, which ended the collaboration with his brother. In 1883 he was called to the chair in Munich vacated by von Siebold, famed for his discoveries on parthenogenesis and the life cycle of parasitic worms. Here he remained to his death in 1937. Between 1870 and 1889 the famous memoirs by the collaborating brothers appeared. In view of their completely different natures and temperaments, it is difficult to conceive how this collaboration was carried out. It might be safe to assume that Oscar led in the theoretical planning and analysis while Richard accounted for the carefulness of the observations, the exhaustiveness of the study, and, probably, the choice of the material.

One of the first fruits was the remarkable monograph on the nervous system and the sense organs of the medusae, a very difficult subject in the absence of specific methods, which they exhausted so completely (in 1877–78) that for many decades practically nothing was added to the results. In the following year, the same was performed for *Actinia*. It is remarkable how Richard Hertwig remained attached to this group of sea anemones. Though never a taxonomist, he later accepted the task of writing the monograph on the *Actinia* of the "Challenger" Expedition. When I worked as a student in his laboratory and, in the systematic study, came to the group of *Actinia*, he was so enthusiastic that he made me work for weeks on the arrangement of the septa in aberrant forms, a topic for which I could not summon any enthusiasm. With him it was obviously a sentimental return to his *vieux amours*.

The next famous common work established in 1878 the theory of the germ layers and their application to the understanding of the relations between medusae and hydroids. This work led directly to another classic, the establishment of the coelom theory and the theory of the mesoderm (1882), one of the great cornerstones of comparative embryology. A little later the brothers returned to the sea urchin egg, which Oscar had made famous, and did the first systematic experiments on hybridization in this group (1886). This work was followed by classical experiments on fertilization and cleavage under abnormal conditions, and a paper (1887) which was to start a flood of experiments with this ideal material. Among the discoveries was the first successful experiment in chemical parthenogenesis of the sea urchin egg. Thus the Hertwigs became also the first experimental embryologists.

Though Richard Hertwig never returned to this kind of experimentation, the sea urchin egg and its doings remained his love, more than even the *Actinia*. When, fifteen years later, I was his assistant, the most exciting part of the term was the week in which the fertilization and cleavage of the living sea urchin egg were demonstrated in the elementary course, which was taken mostly by premedical students and future high school teachers. Munich was far away from the Mediterranean across the Alps, and it was quite a feat at that time (without refrigeration, motor cars, or airplanes) to ship the mature sea urchins with the necessary local sea water. There was great excitement for weeks until finally the crates arrived safely and were carried up the steep stone stairways of the old monastery to the laboratory on the third floor. Immediately after unpacking, the first test fertilizations were made and the important animals were put into aquaria and cared for like babies. Until the decisive day, new fertilizations were tried all the time and the normalcy of development checked. Egg batches were put into different temperatures and sea waters of different composition were tried, and the major part of all these activities (most of which were as enthusiastic as they were unnecessary) was carried out by Hertwig himself. The tenseness increased; the anxiety as to whether the demonstration would be successful gripped the whole laboratory; and finally the great day came. The class started at two o'clock, and up to that time one nervous check after the other was made. Hertwig himself came to the institute before seven in the morning to try the first fertilization. I remember arriving in the morning and finding the boss already sitting collecting eggs. "You are late today," he said. I answered, "But it is only eight o'clock." Reproachfully he retorted, "Yes, but on fertilization day one rises early." Years later at one of his jubilees we performed a skit (to the authorship of which I must confess) lampooning the goings-on of fertilization day. Hertwig was played beautifully by a young student, and his own family surprised him by playing themselves in a domestic scene before fertilization day. The best actor was Carl Gruber in the role of a visiting Japanese scientist.

Returning to the eighties of the last century, Richard, after separating from Oscar, turned more and more to protozoa. His first great performance was an extended study of the Radiolaria which first proved that these organisms are unicellular and cleared up their specific structure. The material was again collected in a fishing village on the Mediterranean shore (actually near Messina in Sicily) without the benefit of a laboratory, though at that time the great station at Naples was already available. Unfortunately for both sides, a rift between the great founder of the Naples station, Anton Dohrn, and the brothers Hertwig had occurred, though neither was responsible for it. The Hertwigs had come to Naples, if I remember correctly the story given me by Richard

Hertwig, on their return from Messina with its famous radiolarian fauna. At the station they met with a jolly crowd of young zoologists, headed by the meteoric genius Kleinenberg, who after brilliant beginnings—his work on *Hydra* and on the trochophore theory—was to be murdered by a bandit in Sicily. I can imagine that the brothers Hertwig were overserious and unwilling to share in the boisterous conviviality. This made them unpopular with the bohemian Kleinenberg group, and Kleinenberg wrote a poetic lampooning of the Hertwigs as examples of ridiculous sissies and bad sports. This product was circulated at the station and fell into the hands of the victims. They made Dohrn responsible for it, certainly unreasonably, and never set foot into the station any more. Even their students were discouraged, to their great disadvantage, so that I myself, for example, went to Naples first after Anton Dohrn's death, and thus was deprived of the chance of meeting this great man. Kleinenberg's poem, which I never saw, must have been very mean as Richard Hertwig certainly was no spoilsport though very correct and fond of propriety.

Hertwig's most important work of this period was on the conjugation of the infusoria, in which he filled the gaps Bütschli had left thirteen years earlier, a study to which hardly anything was added later on the morphological side. For decades afterward he used infusoria for different kinds of experimental attack, and on his table there were always some watch crystal cultures, in the keeping of which he was a master. His purely morphological work with protozoa ended with the classic paper on *Actino-*

sphaerium (1898), where for the first time, outside of the group of infusoria and sporozoa, a complicated life cycle was demonstrated and the cytological details of mitosis, reduction divisions, and fertilization were worked out and beautifully illustrated. For a long time this animal also remained for him an important experimental material, the culture of which he had mastered completely, and as a young assistant I spent many an hour learning the technique in order to take over when he was absent.

Before coming to the work of Hertwig's mature and still later years, I should describe his laboratory and teaching as I first found it in 1898. In this year I had taken my premedical examinations and intended to go on with medicine just long enough to pass the medical board, but to devote all the time I could spare to zoological work and get my Ph.D. on the side. As I wanted to see another university and other professors, I decided upon Munich and went there more than a month ahead of the term. I called upon Hertwig and explained to him my problem. With his typical friendliness and helpfulness, he invited me to enter the laboratory at once, during vacation time, and to work full day as long as my time permitted. It turned out that I stayed on for good after the first medical clinics I attended convinced me that I should never become a physician while a nice, clean, cozy zoological laboratory was nearby as a haven. There were not more than six young zoologists in the laboratory at that time, mostly busy with a doctor's thesis (Max Hartmann one of them), when I started with what I have described as the "big practicum." There was no day on which Hertwig did not come twice to my table, bringing material or literature, advising on techniques, and checking my slides. Thus the work became most interesting. Having watched the work in Bütschli's laboratory, I planned to go through with the full course, but this was very difficult because of Hertwig's easily aroused enthusiasm. Whenever in the course of the work an observation was made which looked new, Hertwig became deeply interested and insisted on starting research on the subject. Thus I had reached, in my climb up the phylogenetic tree, only the Foraminifera, when a feature seen in one of my slides made Hertwig start me on the study of the propagation of this group. Fortunately (because I never could have succeeded at that time and far from the seashore with the difficult problem) the material became scarce, and I was able to continue my course work. This lasted up to *Hydra*, when tissue maceration revealed some strange stages of the development of cnidocysts. After some work I dug up a Russian paper in which these stages were pictured, and again I could go on. When I reached the cestodes I was incautious enough to demonstrate to Hertwig some strange-looking stages of the development of the scolices of *Echinococcus*. This time his enthusiasm was justified, and I embarked upon a little piece of research, my first, which was published the following year. But, realizing that by this method I should never finish an orderly zoological education, I returned to Heidelberg to go through Bütschli's intensive course before starting on a thesis. When I returned four years later as Hertwig's assistant and had to supervise the courses, I took care that the students fin-

Richard Hertwig, 1902 (Photograph by author)

Mr. and Mrs. Richard Hertwig on their golden wedding anniversary, 1936

View from the old Munich laboratory toward the Cathedral
of Our Lady and the cloisters of St. Michael's, 1930

ished their laboratory education before starting with research, though this meant much wrestling with Hertwig
and his quick enthusiasm.

The old Zoological Institute in Munich, which was at
that time beginning to develop into probably the greatest
research center in zoology, thanks to the attraction exercised by Hertwig the zoologist and Hertwig the teacher
and friend, deserves a short description. It occupied a
wing of the Old Academy, a monastery of the seventeenth
century, the destruction of which in the last war is a great
loss. The Old Academy was a large block of big buildings
with thick walls surrounding a series of courtyards, one
corner of which was occupied by the rather beautiful St.
Michael's church. The Zoological Institute occupied the
third floor in the posterior courtyard, and from its windows one had a most beautiful view of the nave of the
church and the adjoining cloisters with the grandiose
background of the two characteristic "onion towers" of
the great cathedral (see illustration). The students' laboratory was one large room with a vaulted ceiling sup-
ported by marble columns. Three large windows showed
the just-described view. There were three more small
rooms and the two rooms of the professor. Along this row
of rooms stretched a long narrow corridor with innumerable windows toward another courtyard. Here the laboratory courses for premedics were held and the aquaria
were set up. Though the building was located in the center
of the city, complete quiet ruled, and the old monastic
atmosphere had a special charm in this oasis of learning.
Later, when the institute work grew immensely, two adja-

cent wings were added. From these premises a corridor led into the zoological museum, which occupied the street front of the building and what once had been the common rooms of the monastery. The ornithological collection, for example, was exhibited in the monks' old refectory, a beautiful hall with gorgeous baroque decorations. The museum, a rather good one for the time, was also under the directorship of Richard Hertwig. He took this duty very seriously and occupied himself with all the important problems. With the all-around training of that time he was well posted in taxonomy and made a good museum director, though it was only a sideline of his work. The administration of this museum also required quite a bit of diplomacy. It was very popular with the Bavarian court. The sister of the regent, Princess Therese, was a trained taxonomist. She was frequently found in the premises looking over materials to compare with her own collections made on a South American expedition. Other princes were great hunters and gave their quarry, brought from the Caucasus or Altai, to the museum, expecting it to be exhibited in a prominent place. It was not always easy for Hertwig, although he was himself a strong monarchist, to deal with these royal highnesses and to keep in good standing even when the specimens were not good enough for exhibition. Later one of Hertwig's old students, the protozoologist and ecologist Doflein, was made subdirector and, being a very good diplomat and a favorite of the court, managed the administration most successfully.

I cannot resist the temptation to introduce, at this point, a short detour on royal amateur zoologists and protectors of zoology, especially as at one point Richard Hertwig is also involved.

During the Middle Ages and up to the eighteenth century, princes of all kinds not only were protectors of the sciences but frequently were deeply and actively interested in the work of their protégés. In the thirteenth century the Emperor Frederick II wrote what amounts to a handbook of ornithology. Galileo's work was followed in every detail by the ruling Medici and the ruling Pope, not to mention all the other princes and nobles all over Europe. After the French Revolution science became more and more independent of the protection of the rulers, and where the princes and nobles took over the patronage it was more as a social form than because of an intellectual interest. I have mentioned the foundation of the Kaiser Wilhelm Research Institutes by the Kaiser, who certainly was completely devoid of any interest in chemistry or biology but simply acted as was supposed to be proper for a monarch. I once had a chance to observe him closely in his role of protector of science. When the new institute for A. Wassermann was inaugurated in 1913, the ceremony took place in the engine room of the physicochemical institute, and the chairs had to be placed as the big machines permitted. Thus I found myself only a few steps from the Kaiser and facing him. He made a theatrical entree before being seated, and I could not help feeling that this much-discussed monarch did not act with the natural poise of one born to the throne and convinced that this had happened by God's grace. The impression was rather of somebody who tried to play the role of an emperor by overacting.

It was customary that at the occasion of the inauguration of a new Kaiser Wilhelm Institute the festival lecture should deal with the subject of research of the next planned institute, which, in this case, was the biological one. Thus Richard Hertwig had been invited to deliver the address. He chose as his topic sex determination and, obviously with the friendly intention of boosting my position in the new institute, talked at length about my then new work on intersexuality in *Lymantria dispar*. The Kaiser sat there with all signs of boredom. But, when Hertwig described how these intersexes behave sexually as if they did not know whether they are females or males, the Kaiser roared with laughter, to return at once to his boredom. I did not like this, though I would have roared with laughter myself if some prophet had told me that at the time of inauguration of our institute the same Kaiser would be chopping wood in Holland.

This introduction was to lead to the remarkable fact that a large number of crowned and not-crowned princes have been ardent amateur zoologists. I have already mentioned the Bavarian Wittelsbach family and Princess Therese, the sister of the regent. She actually spent most of her time arranging and determining her collections and came regularly to the museum to compare notes. The museum curators were malicious enough to say that her specimens of butterflies showed the fingerprints of the flunkeys who caught them. Though it is not probable that the elderly, refined lady had done much running after the animals in the jungles of Brazil, the men who did the gossiping would themselves probably have collected with the aid of natives. Actually the Princess was very serious about her work, and I can testify to the intelligence and alertness of the questions she put after the many lectures she attended. It was probably her influence which made one of the younger princes, Conrad, start a serious study of zoology. I do not know whether he was really interested or just wanted to occupy himself, as the life of a secundo-geniture prince must be rather boring. He did his work quite faithfully, but I must say that I did not like his presence in my classes. I was supposed to address him as Your Royal Highness and in the third person, but this seemed so ridiculous when I was explaining a dissection that I could not do it and used the simple "you," which was not welcome. I was at that time rather unpolitical and, if anything, something of a monarchist like most unpolitical Germans. I did not feel any qualms in address-ing dignified and noble old Princess Therese in the proper way, but it choked me to do so with a silly princeling. A few years later the revolution came, and the prince dis-appeared for the rest of his life in a monastery.

The best-known royal zoologist is of course the Em-peror of Japan. Even before his ascension to the throne he had a laboratory in the palace and employed good bi-ologists as his collaborators. There is no doubt that he took his work seriously, and I should not be surprised if he preferred it considerably to his imperial duties. He liked to collect marine specimens and had them determined by specialists if he did not himself do the taxonomic work. He also tried to keep informed about general biological problems by ordering Japanese and other scholars to give him private lectures on their work. I once was sounded out as to whether I would do this, and a talk in French was tentatively arranged. But for certain reasons it did not come off, and thus I missed the chance of finding out directly how far his information went. Judging from the reticent hints of his collaborators, however, he certainly would have become a zoologist if he had not been born to the throne.

It is less well known that the wily and intelligent politician, the former King Ferdinand of Bulgaria, was a passionate zoologist. He kept a museum in his palace and employed a former student of mine, Buresch, as a custodian. He was said to be an excellent entomologist, though I never heard of interests in general biology. But the fact that he sent his custodian abroad to acquire general zoological knowledge suggests broader interests in keeping with his generally known high intelligence. Moreover his son, later Czar Boris, was brought up in this tradition, continued the palace museum, and was especially interested in Lepidoptera. Once I almost found out the extent of his knowledge. He was visiting in Berlin, and his ambassador, my friend Methodi Popoff, also a former student, gave a reception. When my turn came to be presented, the King came forward, shook hands, and said, "I have wished for a long time to meet you, because I was so much interested in your work on *Lymantria.* . . ." At this moment a door opened and in came Chancellor Stresemann. Seeing this, the King left me without finishing his sentence and retired with Stresemann into a corner for political talk. Thus I never found out whether he really knew my work or had only been told about it ten minutes before, as is the way of kings.

A rather well-known potentate zoologist was the Prince of Monaco, whom one was told to address as *Votre Altesse Seigneurale.* He certainly had not much to rule in his tiny principality and thus had time for his hobby, which was oceanography and deep-sea zoology. There is no doubt that he was a real expert in these fields and did serious work with the assistance of his zoological helper, Mr. Richard. His yacht "Alice," a beautiful ship which I once visited, was completely fitted for deep-sea expeditions, and he participated in many cruises as an active scientist. The numerous volumes on his expeditions bear witness to the seriousness of the work. He even looked very much like a French professor, with an immense mustache above a short beard and a serious face. His greatest performance was the building of the big oceanographic institute standing high above steep rocks and occupying the most beautiful and conspicuous site in Monaco. It was lavishly appointed and is still today not only a landmark but a center of re-search for visiting zoologists and oceanographers, though the old prince is long dead.

One more royal biologist, this one not belonging to a ruling family, may be mentioned though he was more of a geographer and general patron of the natural sciences than an active zoologist. When I worked almost fifty years ago at the zoological station of Banyuls near the border of Spain at the Gulf of Lyons, the boat, a big, broad fishing vessel, was called "Roland" after Prince Roland Bonaparte, who had given it to the station. At the laboratory it was generally called "Roulant" (the rolling one), and I can testify from dire experience in dredging expeditions that it amply deserved its name. Later I met the donor in his capacity of patron to the sciences in his Paris mansion, which I mention because it contained the most beautiful private library I have ever seen. Attached to the reception room was a quadrangle of broad galleries stacked to the ceiling with beautifully bound books, mostly on travel and expeditions, and series of monographs. The center was occupied by antique tables bearing old globes and nautical instruments. It must have been a remarkable man, apart from the necessary wealth, who brought together such a collection. But let us return again to Richard Hertwig.

At the end of the century Hertwig returned to the experimental cytological work of which he had been the pioneer in his youth. In his work on protozoa he had developed the art of exact culturing starting from a single individual, what was later called a clone. The observations he made on growth rhythms and so-called depressions led him to ask the meaning of growth, multiplication, fertilization, age, and death. He studied his cultures of *Actinosphaerium* and *Paramecium* under different temperatures and food conditions and checked upon the rate of reproduction and nuclear changes, work which became the starting point for a whole science. He became so immersed in this that he could hardly think of anything else. I remember approaching him one day about some laboratory matters to which he listened absentmindedly, his glasses pushed up on his forehead and a crystal with a culture in his hands. When I had finished he said, "But I have an actinosphaerium, which. . . ." He was much impressed at that time with the finding of extra-nuclear "chromatin" in *Actinosphaerium*, which he studied under his name of chromidia in the different phases of the life of this heliozoon, believing that many secrets of cell physiology were hidden behind the facts. But later he turned mostly to the plasmatic and nuclear cycles of *Paramecium*, which led him to the establishment of the doctrine of nucleoplasmic ratio (simultaneously sponsored by Boveri on a different basis). He soon came to believe that the nucleoplasmic ratio was responsible for cell division and growth but also for age and death. A large body of experiments, in which his student Popoff also figured prominently, was performed, and many important facts were discovered, like the difference in cytoplasmic and nuclear growth between divisions, which was assumed to lead to a tension that was solved by a sudden nuclear growth leading to cell division. It was this new type of experimental cytology which at that time (1900–14) attracted so many students from all over the world to the Munich laboratory. Before that time Hertwig had had the usual small number of zoology students, many of whom became leaders in their own right, like Plate, Brauer, Hofer, Boveri, Doflein, Hartmann. But after 1900 the numbers increased so that sometimes as many as thirty-five research workers crowded the institute—students doing their doctor's thesis as well as foreign visitors who had already started their careers in their respective countries. If I mention only those who themselves became leaders in their respective fields, and include also those who did their thesis or research work with me but had, of course, come to Munich attracted by the fame of Hertwig, there were: the protozoologists Awerinzeff, Dobell, Ivanic, Jollos, McKinnon, Moroff, Neresheimer, Reichenow, Swarzewsky, Wenyon; the pathologists Howard, Tyzzer, Rössle; the zoologists Buchner, Chambers, Erdmann, von Frisch, Heiss, Katsuki, Köhler, Kuschakewitsch, Marcus, Nachtsheim, Papanikolau, Popoff, Popovici, Philipchenko, Rimsky-Korsakoff, Schaxel, Schellenberg, Schwangart, Seiler, Witschi. This sounds more like a honor roll than a list of students, and there were in addition many who would have been included in this group if fate had permitted them to continue their work, and many others who became successful specialists in other fields, e.g., the fisheries.

In the early years of the century Hertwig conceived the idea that sex determination might also have to do with the nucleoplasmic ratio, as the sperm is almost all nucleus while the mature egg has only a very small one. This somewhat wild idea led to large-scale experimentation by Hertwig and his students on sex in frogs and also in such organisms as *Hydra, Dinophilus,* and others. Though it turned out later that sex determination could only be understood genetically, and Hertwig's own material, the frog, was finally also explained in these terms by his student Witschi, a very large body of facts was discovered, e.g., the remarkable sex races, the transformation of the gonads in some races, and the direct development in others. These and many other facts led to the establishment of the final solution only when new genetic ideas, conceived for another object, pointed the way. Hertwig himself was immediately ready to accept the new solution though it meant relinquishing his own pet ideas. At the height of his experiments Hertwig's enthusiasm upset the entire laboratory. He had only the most primitive, home-built apparatus for the elevation at constant temperature of the thousands of tadpoles. This caused unending excitement, inundations, critical rises or drops in temperatures. Many nights Hertwig got up at two or three o'clock, walked the mile to the laboratory, and checked upon the unreliable apparatus. One night one of his students—I think it was Chambers—dreamed that all his valuable polliwogs were being cooked because of a failure of the thermostat. He rushed to the laboratory after midnight and arrived just in time to save the experiment; the thermostat really had failed. Thus everybody was happy when the frog season ended and Hertwig settled down to normal life without daily excitement.

At this time a great disaster befell the Hertwig family and changed their lives for years. On my arrival in the institute one day while Hertwig and his wife were in the United States attending the international zoological congress, the old *Diener* showed me a morning paper with the news that the Hertwigs' two sons had met with an Alpine accident. I found out where they had been brought and set out to reach them, in a hut high up in the Tyrolean Alps. The younger son was only bruised, but the older one had a head injury and was lying unconscious in the shabby bed. The Tyrolean country doctor who was in attendance assured me that it was nothing but a severe concussion of the brain which would blow over within a few days. During a night vigil I found the boy raving with fantasies and realized that he must be in a much worse condition than the doctor claimed. In the morning I went down to the valley and telegraphed a Munich surgeon, who departed at once and arrived at night in the mountain refuge. He found that a piece of the skull the size of a silver dollar had been crushed out of the skull and pushed into the brain. We brought the boy down under considerable difficulties, and an operation was successful. Hertwig, who had been informed by cable, left immediately for Europe. At that time there was as yet no wireless, and he was without news of the operation during the endless steamer trip. The boy slowly recovered but had lost his memory and many other associations. Miraculously everything came back, however, and after a year he was able to take up his university work again as an unusually gifted student. One day when he was sailing on a lake near Berlin, the boat capsized and he was drowned, though a good swimmer. Possibly the mast had hit the covered spot in his skull. For four days the father was out with the fishermen dragging the lake bottom until they finally recovered the body. Hertwig never recovered from this ordeal. For years he suffered from insomnia and was in a haze during the day so that much of the laboratory work had to be taken off his shoulders. But he never missed a lecture or a day in the laboratory. Finally his doctor persuaded him to take a leave, and he went for half a year to Tenerife in the Canary Islands, where he fished in the old way, as in Haeckel's days, for his beloved Radiolaria and regained his strength.

In the classic Greek theater a tragedy was always followed by a gaudy satyr play. So I may be excused if I insert here a little, slightly ridiculous story which was an outcome of Hertwig's insomnia. The oldest student in the laboratory was an apothecary, over fifty years old, who owned a successful pharmacy in the Philippines. At that time everybody of consequence in Germany had a doctor's title, and the wives were addressed as *Frau Doktor*. Mrs. K greatly resented the fact that her husband did not have a degree and that she could not be called *Frau Doktor* at the *Kaffeeklatsch* or in the German Club. Thus she made her rather henpecked husband go to Europe for a few years to try for a doctor's degree when he was already fifty-four years old. As he had collected specimens in the Philippines and sent them to the Munich Museum, zoology appeared to be the proper field. Thus he registered in our laboratory, took all the courses, and, under Hertwig's guidance, finally finished with many headaches a decent piece of experimental work on sex in *Hydra*. Then he wrote up his material, which had been deemed acceptable, into a thesis which he delivered to Hertwig. One day when I came to Hertwig's room I found him all wrought up, and he told me that K had handed him a completely impossible thesis, misinterpreting the experiments and generally writing nonsense. He had returned it to him for rewriting. But the second edition had the same fate and was again returned. The K's were terribly upset, he, because he thought he had done his very best, and she, because she felt the danger to her *Frau Doktor* aspirations. Thus he came to me in search of help. Since the work, like most thesis work at that time, had been more or less directed by me, I knew that it could be written up as a satisfactory thesis, for the experimental results were all right. Thus I softened to K's entreaties and promised to help him. One evening my wife and I went to K's apartment and enjoyed thoroughly a dinner of roast goose stuffed with chestnuts washed down with a fine Rhine wine. After dinner K and I retired, and, using his records, I dictated the thesis to him. This was, of course, all wrong; but I really pitied the poor old man who had finished an acceptable piece of work, and I knew that Hertwig, owing to his worries, was harder on him than necessary. K handed the manuscript to Hertwig. The next day, when I entered his room, the boss called out, "Now I have enough of K. Again he has written the same nonsense as before." Somewhat taken aback, I asked which parts he meant, and he told me, "Here and there he writes this confused stuff." I intimated cautiously that this might be an error, and the manuscript was consulted. Of course the "nonsense" was not there. Finally it turned out that Hertwig had read the paper in bed during a sleepless night and, not being completely awake, had mixed it in his waking memory with the contents of the former drafts. Mrs. K became *Frau Doktor*, and I am not as ashamed of the little trick as I should be.

The great period of the Munich laboratory ended with the First World War. Though Hertwig kept his chair until his seventy-fifth year, he did not accomplish much more research though he wrote a very remarkable book on evolution, trying to bring the new insight from genetics into line with his old Darwinian beliefs. In addition he kept very active in scientific and other organizations and never took any rest. After his retirement his successor von Frisch was finally able to build a modern institute with Rockefeller Foundation funds, and a room was reserved for Richard Hertwig where he worked daily, literally to the last day of his life. He had returned to his old love, the Radiolaria, and begun to study the material he had collected in Tenerife. When he died in his eighty-seventh year a slide was under the microscope, and on the table was a drawing which he had not completely finished the day before.

There can be no doubt that Hertwig was the greatest teacher of professional zoologists of his time. This influence was exercised mainly in his laboratory. Like all German professors of zoology, he had to give the big lectures on zoology and comparative anatomy which the premedical students also had to take. The summer term lectures took place every morning from seven to eight o'clock, which did not disturb Hertwig, who was an early riser. One cannot say that he was a good lecturer. He spoke slowly and monotonously, and in spite of his mastery of the subject it was tiresome to listen. Thus his superb qualities as a teacher came out only in the laboratory, where the personal approach counted. Nevertheless he also exercised a great influence upon the teaching of zoology through his textbook, which went through numerous editions over a series of decades and was translated into all languages. It must have been used by hundreds of thousands of students, thanks to its simplicity, clarity, and richness of material in relatively small space. Every new edition was very carefully revised and brought up to date. I can testify to this as I helped to read the proofs for a number of them.

The secret of Hertwig's success in the laboratory was his immense human interest in every one of his students, to whom he was like a father and friend. There was no part of their work, including the menial tasks, into which he would not enter and give a helping hand. He was always ready to suggest new lines of approach and even to try them out first himself. There was a constant collaboration between the professor and the advanced student, who thus got all the benefits of his experience, knowledge, skill, and enthusiasm, while the whole group worked like a family, each member helping the other.

This great humanity of Hertwig might be called a democratic attitude were it not for the fact that he was politically a great reactionary. During the First World War he went so far as to work for the wildly Pan-Germanistic, jingoistic Fatherlands party, a fact which is difficult to reconcile with his mildness, affability, and humanitarian attitude. He was always ready to help and to give freely to good causes. Many a poor student had his fees returned and the cost of the doctorate paid by Hertwig. With his employees he was just as friendly as with his students. In spite of his political extremism he was deeply interested in all civic affairs, especially those of a cultural type, and here he was as progressive and liberal as possible. He played a considerable role in the university extension movement, which was a completely private organization run by men like him. He spent an unbelievable amount of time on the organization of popular science lectures for the laymen and himself gave such evening courses. All of us younger men had to participate, and he not only suggested the topics but attended the classes to see how they were done. These classes, for which a nominal fee was charged, were frequently large ones, sometimes with hundreds of hearers. About three quarters of the participants were working people of all kinds, the rest grammar school teachers, retired officers, businessmen, and usually a sprinkling of priests and nuns. After the lecture came a period of answering questions, which were written out and put into a box while the lecturer left the room for a while. Frequently the questions were very clever, and the lecturer had to use his wits to answer them. Altogether, Hertwig, who was one of the driving forces, accomplished much for this type of adult education and really democratic action. In another way he did the same when he participated in the founding of a laymen's science society. It met once a fortnight in a hall accommodating almost a thousand members to hear a popular science lecture by a well-known, frequently excellent speaker. For years Hertwig presided himself and did most of the work to engage good speakers. He even remained after the lecture for the usual social gathering where the lecture was discussed over a glass of beer, though the beer-hall atmosphere was repugnant to him. In the same way he gave unstintingly of his time and energy for any kind of progressive civic activity, his great liberalism in action somehow being completely unrelated to his reactionary political beliefs.

It is obvious that a man of such qualities would be much sought after and could not escape being made the president of practically all imaginable societies. Hertwig took such positions very seriously and usually did much more work than was expected, never employing a secretary, by the way. He delivered the necessary addresses, carefully prepared and couched in cultured language, and made all the innumerable after-dinner speeches expected from him. Needless to say, he received all the honors coming to such a man, including being knighted, and he enjoyed them in a natural, perfectly simple way. He took great pleasure in social intercourse, and the hospitality of his house was extended to all of his students. He loved art and music, and one met him at all good concerts. In his younger years I heard him playing the piano. His general erudition was high, based, as with most Germans of that time, upon the classics. In his old days he was still at home with Latin and Greek and the arts of Rome and Greece. But his greatest asset remained his humanity and friendly feeling for the younger generation. An example of this may conclude the reminiscences of a great pioneer of science. I had been proposed for a promotion which meant tenure and the right to a pension and therefore was very important for me. There were certain political difficulties and intrigues by other professors who wanted the rare job for one of their men, and thus the decision by the ministry of education took a long time and had not yet arrived when Christmas approached. On Christmas Eve, when no German would voluntarily leave his house and family, Hertwig had a telephone call from the ministry saying that I had been promoted, and he left the celebration and walked a mile to my home in the wintry night to bring me personally the good tidings. It is such little things which describe a man better than all biographical oratory.

I cannot end the description of the great teachers and laboratories in Heidelberg and Munich without a short memorial to one remarkable group of students who flocked to both of these laboratories, the Russian students. This was in the days of the czars, when Russia produced not only degenerate grand dukes and illiterate peasants but also a relatively small layer of unusually refined and cultured men, among them many scientists. In both Bütschli's and Hertwig's laboratories a number of these were always to be found, usually men who had already started their university careers in Russia and came to the famous German laboratories for inspiration, sometimes also to take an additional degree. Many of these, in both places, became my friends for life, and I owe them many an hour of interesting discussion and many moments of friendly intercourse. All of them were unusual men of high erudition and culture with whom you could discuss almost anything, and in addition they were fine zoologists who knew the facts and problems and could talk interestingly about them. All of them fitted beautifully into the group and were considered welcome and valuable guests. Only one of them is still alive, Novikoff, who, after fleeing all over Europe before bolshevism, finally was able to live out his long life in this country. Among the many I may mention Schewiakoff, one of the oldest students of Bütschli, an excellent protozoologist who later was very unpopular among the liberal Russian scientists when he became undersecretary of education and a tool of czarist bureaucratic oppression. Strangely enough he survived the revolution and was still a professor in Siberia under Lenin. There was the brilliant Nicolai Koltzoff, probably the best Russian zoologist of the last generation, an amiable, unbelievably cultured and clear-thinking scholar, admired by everybody who knew him. He came frequently to western laboratories, and we were friends from my student days. In the early years of Leninism he was condemned to death because of alleged relations with the White Army and was said to have escaped execution only because the hangmen grew tired of their work. In time he was reinstated and was able to build up the biggest and most modern institute of experimental biology in Russia, where fundamental genetics, long neglected in Russia, also found a home. But in spite of this prominent position Koltzoff had to be very cautious, as he was closely watched. When I visited Moscow in 1929 he put his apartment in the institute at my disposition, but he himself left town under some pretext. Evidently he could not dare to be seen with a foreigner. Soon afterward our correspondence stopped, obviously because he was forbidden to write abroad. He lived to see the existence of his institute threatened by Lysenko but died before the final victory of this agronomist. His brilliant wife, a scientist in her own right, followed him voluntarily.

A different fate was that of S. Kuschakewitsch, for a long time a member of the Munich zoological family. An excellent all-around zoologist, he was a refined and sensitive man behind his six-foot-ten-inch frame, deeply interested in art, especially that of classical antiquity, which he studied during long sojourns in Naples. He was a most pleasant traveling companion, always helpful and cheerful, and we had some glorious experiences together, like ascending Etna during an eruption. When the revolution came in Russia he was a professor in Moscow. He joined the antibolshevist forces and, after their defeat, reached Turkey with the remnants of the White Army. While still a young man, he succumbed in Istanbul to typhus.

Another type was J. Philipchenko, a fine biologist and one of the first successful Russian geneticists. He died relatively young in Leningrad, where he had a good institute within the precincts of the former czar's summer palace. I visited there one winter and had the rather bourgeois experience of being driven by a Cossack in a sleigh pulled like a whirlwind by one of the famous Orloff trotters of the czar. In spite of Philipchenko's antibolshevism, which he professed too openly for his safety, he died a natural death before the rise of Lysenko.

I cannot mention all these refined and cultured Russian scholars of the old school with whom I made friends in the Heidelberg and Munich laboratories. Only three or four more may be noted. Boris Sukatschoff was an excellent embryologist, but more impressive because of his cultured personality. With his unusually refined wife he was the center of our group of students. They introduced me and others to the Russian type of "bull sessions" so beautifully and dramatically described by Gorki in the story of his youth. This meant a gathering, lasting through most of the night, around the steaming samovar, with innumerable cups of tea and thin, homemade Russian cigarettes; and excited discussions of all problems of heaven and earth, sometimes deep and philosophical, sometimes emotional and sentimental, but always intensive and fascinating. In Bütschli's laboratory at the same time worked Kassianoff, a good zoologist and gentle, sweet personality with a good deal of the old Russian emotional constitution. In his young years he inherited a big business in Charbin (Manchuria) and left science to become a multimillionaire. When the Japanese occupied Manchuria they robbed him of almost all of his fortune, and he was glad to escape to Shanghai and finally spend his last years in Berkeley, where we met again after a lifetime. What strange twists of fate have happened in these times. In Berkeley he found a third member of Bütschli's scientific family of forty years before, Bütschli's long-time assistant and confidante, Clara Hamburger, who after a turn in a Nazi concentration camp had finally landed in Berkeley where she ended her life working as a seamstress, too proud to accept much help from her relatives.

A very unequal couple of friends from these old times were A. Rimsky-Korsakoff and W. Redikorzew. The first, a son of the composer, was a first-class entomologist and otherwise a quiet and refined scholar. His mild manners and good nature made him a pleasant but not exciting companion. Redikorzew, who became a good museum zoologist and an authority on some invertebrate groups, was a completely different type. He had the exterior of a Russian peasant and, though highly cultured, tried to appear unconcerned about scholarship and erudition. He was full of wit and a most entertaining companion. He had the gift of drawing beautiful cartoons which always hit the point and were most amusingly conceived and executed. He was a very strong character who stood by his convictions. I had the pleasure of seeing both these fine men a last time before the iron curtain went down tightly. With Rimsky-Korsakoff I kept up correspondence, cautiously written on open post cards and containing nothing that might endanger him with his Red masters. Only a short time ago I read in the press that he died an octogenarian. The last card I received from him before the iron curtain clanged down contained the words: "I feel rather lonely since Redikorzew is not longer with us." What did this mean? Liquidation? Siberia? I fear the worst, having known Redikorzew's uncompromising honesty. Probably this noble type of Russian scholars and gentlemen of the old school has disappeared forever, except for the few still surviving in this country, like my old friend A. Petrunkewitsch, a former student of Weismann, one of the few classics of that time whom I by chance never met. I think that all these men deserve a grateful, appreciative, and heartfelt memorial.

Theodor Boveri, the Last Classic

Asides: M. BOVERI, H. HENKING

At the end of the classic period of zoology and especially cytology stands Theodor Boveri, who finished what Bütschli, the Hertwigs, Strasburger, Flemming, and Van Beneden had started and, in addition, became one of the pioneers of the modern developments. He had been one of the first students of Richard Hertwig and thus continued the great pedigree whose ancestor had been Johannes Müller as a powerful branch, from which his students like Mrs. Boveri, Spemann, Baltzer, von Ubisch, and again their students like Mangold, Holtfreter, Hamburger, were to continue the amazing line, just as did others of the Hertwigs' students. Theodor Boveri's external life was as simple as that of the other great men we have mentioned. He was born in 1862 in Bamberg of a well-known family to which the great Swiss and German industrialists known as Brown and Boveri belonged. (Another native of Bamberg, Johann Faber, had invented the word microscope about 220 years earlier.) Boveri's early education was the usual humanistic one. Afterward he went to Munich, where he became R. Hertwig's student and took his Ph.D. degree with a thesis on the structure of nerve fibers, a subject to which he never returned. Two years later he became *Privatdocent* in Munich. During these years as student and docent he was so lucky as to be completely free of material worries. He was first selected as one of the honor students of the Catholic faith whom the Bavarian state housed and fed—together with the aristocratic youths destined to become court pages—in a huge building across the Isar River, the Maximilianeum, still a landmark of beautiful Munich. After four years there he received another good fellowship, the Froment grant, also reserved for Bavarian Catholic scientists, which he held for another five years, thus escaping the drudgery of an assistant's job. This left all his time free for research, which was so successful that already in 1893 he was called to Semper's chair in Würzburg, where he stayed for the rest of his too short life.

In 1897 he was married to a fellow zoologist, Marcella O'Grady. The story of their courtship was once told to me by E. B. Wilson, who at that time worked in the laboratory of his friend Boveri. One day an American girl applied for admittance to the laboratory. Up to that time no woman had ever worked in the laboratory, and Boveri, a very shy man, was greatly upset by the prospect. Miss O'Grady arrived and was assigned a room to herself as Boveri thought that she might not like to share a room with men. Every day the professor, according to custom, came to check up on the students' work, and he was very careful to leave the door wide open while he conferred with her. After some months the other students noticed that Boveri closed the door behind him.

He did not marry before going to America to ask for Marcella's hand in the correct, approved way. In 1897 they were married, and Marcella Boveri became his lifelong quiet and efficient collaborator and an excellent cytologist in her own right. They had one daughter. I first saw the Boveris in 1903 when they were hosts to the zoological society. Boveri presented a brilliant review of the status of cytology, while Mrs. Boveri, in her quiet, refined way, was an excellent hostess. At a dinner Carl Chun, the marine zoologist, an excellent and witty speaker, toasted the host and hostess, describing them as the lord and lady of a castle, where she sits all day "bent over her spindle." The intimate collaboration and happy union lasted until Boveri's untimely death in his fifty-third year; his last work, correcting his old work on merogony, was published by Mrs. Boveri. A few years later she returned to her native country and spent the rest of her long life as professor of zoology at Albertus Magnus College in New Haven, worshiped by the girl students and honored by her many friends. It was an unforgettable pleasure to be her guest in the cozy apartment on the campus and to talk about old times and about science while admiring her perfect poise and nobility of bearing and mind.

Returning to Boveri's simple and uneventful life, the only interruptions from the calm and unexciting everyday of a professor in a small, old, and charming university town were vacations on an old family estate, a kind of small chateau, at Hofen, near Bamberg. But what he most enjoyed were the frequent and often long visits to the zoological station in Naples, which was actually his scientific home. He was a friend of Anton Dohrn, with whom not only science but love of the arts forged a strong link. Later he wrote an obituary of Dohrn which is a masterpiece of writing, a noble tribute to a great man by another great one. In Naples he did much of his best work and felt thoroughly at ease and happy. It was here that I saw him the last time. He had taken a long leave and hoped to enjoy a quiet year of work in his beloved south. Whether he knew that he was already a very sick man I do not know. I was passing through Naples on my way to Japan in January, 1914, and he was so kind as to spend the day with me. We talked about many problems, scientific and otherwise, and he was perfectly fresh and intensive. He never mentioned his health, and I could never have guessed that he was already a doomed man. The end came in October, 1915.

Only once in his life was there a really exciting time. It was only a few years before his death. In 1910 the Kaiser decided to celebrate the centenary of Berlin University by founding a society which, endowed with large means, would erect research laboratories for such sciences, mostly border fields, as were not represented in the universities or could not work on a sufficiently large scale within the limited means of a university. The plan had been worked out by the great historian and theologian, Adolf Harnack, and the minister of education, Schmidt-Ott. The Kaiser was enthusiastic and granted that the planned society should be called Kaiser Wilhelm Society and he would be the protector. The story (which is probably not true or only partly so) goes that the Kaiser invited a group of rich industrialists to his yacht, the "Hohenzollern," and did not let them return ashore until they had signed for the millions needed. Actually a sum unheard of in Germany was collected, and the society was started. The Kaiser presented it with its own flag, designed by him, and also with a court uniform of his own design. It had a large membership of rich people, some of whom were interested in basking in the imperial sun and receiving decorations and invitations to court. But many of them meant to build up something new and important for German science and gave freely without social ambitions. First a chemical institute was founded, to become famous by the work of its members Beckmann, Willstätter, Hahn, and Meitner; next came the electrochemical institute built for Fritz Haber, followed by a serological-biochemical one for Wassermann and Neuberg. In 1912 plans were made for a biological institute, and after some delay it was decided that Theodor Boveri should organize it on a larger scale than all the others.

This came to Boveri as quite a shock, as it meant a sudden move into the limelight which was what he least desired. But the honor was too great a one to be waved aside, and so he went to Berlin to talk over the plans. He was asked to present a plan for a large institute with a series of independent departments working in modern fields of biology. All financial details were settled, and Boveri worked out his plan. All this I learned when he appeared one day in Munich, at the time R. Hertwig was in Tenerife, told me the whole story, and invited me to be one of the group by establishing a department of genetics. The others were to be Hans Spemann, Max Hartmann, and Otto Warburg, and he also hoped to be able to include in some capacity his student, F. Baltzer. As an example of Boveri's complete lack of guile, I should like to tell a little anecdote. I should mention first that in my younger days I was involved in a series of polemics, a pastime in which European scientists indulged at that time and which were carried out with no holds barred. I must confess to the sin of having enjoyed too much these silly controversies with their unrestrained tongue lashings. On the afternoon of their visit the Boveris came to tea, and the conversation was, of course, mostly about the exciting offer. When I left the room for a moment, Boveri asked my wife, of all people, quickly and quite seriously, "Do you think that he is a man with whom one can get along?"

While I was working out the plans for my department I did not hear from Boveri for a long time. One day a long and rather depressed letter came. It reported that Boveri had been very sick. While resting in bed he had asked himself whether it was not a mistake to have accepted the big position. He felt happy in Würzburg, where he had many good friends, especially the physicist, Röntgen. He hated to be in the limelight. But worst for him was the idea that he would have to produce at a faster pace than he liked in order to justify the conspicuous position. Why should he change his whole way of life to occupy a position which might require representation and the hated contacts with the bureaucracy? In addition, ugly Prussian Berlin did not appeal to him. Altogether, he wrote, he had decided to return his commission and stay in Würzburg. He did not mention his health, but I wonder whether he did not already feel that something was wrong. Actually he had less than three years left. (A year later the excellent plant geneticist, Correns, was asked to take Boveri's place. Though a classic geneticist in his own way, he could not compare with Boveri, either as a scholar or as a man.)

It is one of the unique features of Boveri's work that

practically every single one of his papers is a major contribution, if not a classic. I could name only two insignificant papers on taxonomy of actinians which he did in his Munich days under the influence of Hertwig's weakness for this group. Very frequently he made a major discovery, reported on it in a footnote or a small notice read in the local scientific society, and only much later published a fully documented paper or monograph. Some of his greatest discoveries were handled this way. I have remarked that Boveri was the last classicist of cytology before he became the pioneer of modern cytology. This statement related to his first papers on the maturation divisions of *Ascaris*, which almost finished what Van Beneden had started. In his cell studies between 1887 and 1891 he first cleared up what happens to the chromosomes in the maturation divisions, describing the tetrads, uni- and bivalent chromosomes, and their movements. To this was added—simultaneously with Van Beneden—the cycle of the centrosomes (his term). He proved that the centrosome is derived from the sperm and showed the relative independence of centrosomes and asters from the happenings in the nucleus. Already in 1889 he tried to prove that the nucleus, especially the chromosomes, is the carrier of heredity. It is known that Roux, Weismann, and O. Hertwig (1883–84) had already identified the chromosomes with Nägeli's idioplasma. In order to prove experimentally that the nucleus alone carries hereditary substance, Boveri first tried experiments on merogony, a subject to which he was to return many times. He also fertilized giant sea urchin eggs with foreign sperm and then removed large parts of the cytoplasm, observing that it made no difference in the result how much cytoplasm was present. With these experiments he started the vast body of work on the sea urchin egg which he was to perform later.

The last steps in the elucidation of the chromosomal cycle were not made by Boveri, who however realized immediately the importance of what he termed conjugation of the chromosomes (synapsis). It was H. Henking who (1889–91) found the correct interpretation, while J. Rückert (1891) elucidated the details in the way they are still understood today. Rückert, much underestimated in the history of cytology, was professor of anatomy in Munich, a strong, somewhat rough personality with a brilliant mind and the exterior—also the income and tastes— of a big businessman. His early cytological work on lamp-brush chromosomes and on meiosis was far ahead of its time. But I cannot mention the work of Henking without rambling off again.

Henking, in this early work on the chromosomal cycle of insects, had also discovered the sex chromosomes and much of their cycle and described the facts correctly, but without realizing the relation to sex. It is known that McClung ten years later conceived the right idea, though the facts were straightened out only by Miss Stevens and E. B. Wilson. Henking, having finished all this work, changed over into fisheries work and became an authority in this field, occupying the highest position in sea fisheries research and administration in Germany. It must have been forty years later, around 1930, when a slightly built old gentleman with white whiskers called on me and introduced himself as the Privy Counselor Professor Doctor Henking. "I have," he said, "retired from forty years of service in the Fisheries Administration and now have time to do a few things I am interested in. In my time I have looked at hundreds of thousands of fishes and it always struck me as strange that they were exactly one-half females and one-half males. There must be something which causes this, and I should like to find out. I have been told that you might help me." A few questions convinced me that Henking had completely forgotten about the work of his young days and had read no cytological literature for forty years, not to speak of genetics. I tried to explain to him the story of the sex chromosomes and added that, of course, he himself was the one to have seen them first. He was completely unresponsive and simply did not know what I was talking about. Then I showed him my book on sex determination and the quotation of his name in the proper place. Finally he took the book with him and left completely bewildered. A few months later a visitor knocked at my door and in came old Professor Henking, saying, "I do not know whether you remember me. I was here a few months ago. I am Professor Henking, who discovered the sex chromosomes."

As early as 1891 Boveri found the strange phenomenon of chromatin diminution in *Ascaris* which made him continue the detailed study of *Ascaris* eggs for many years. He worked out the cell lineage and used natural abnormalities of development to prove that the mosaic egg of *Ascaris* nevertheless behaves like a harmonious equipotential system. He made his famous experiments proving that

Fritz Schaudinn, 1902 (Photograph by author)

Theodor Boveri, 1903

From left to right, standing: Schaudinn, Driesch, Scherffel, Peters, and a student; seated on ground: Prowazek, Kuckuck, Goldschmidt. Rovigno, 1902 (Photograph by Kraskowitz)

diminution is controlled by the cytoplasm in which the nucleus is imbedded, and as late as 1910 he finally published a monograph on the entire story which is one of the classics of experimental embryology and cytology. While working on the *Ascaris* egg in Würzburg, he continued his experiments with sea urchin eggs which resulted in a series of classic papers. I shall mention only the two most important ones. In 1902, returning to some of his own and Driesch's older experiments, he accomplished his amazing proof for the chromosome theory of heredity and the qualitative difference of the chromosomes. Disperm eggs dividing into four blastomeres distribute the three sets of chromosomes in such a way that one, two, three, or four blastomeres receive complete or incomplete sets of chromosomes, with the result that the parts of the larvae derived from blastomeres with incomplete chromosomal sets develop pathologically. The way this analysis is carried out can be regarded as a model for superb and brilliant work. It is hardly understandable that many textbooks of genetics written nowadays omit mention of this classic.

Of equal greatness was the work on the nucleoplasmic ratio which soon followed (1905). Already in 1889 Boveri had noticed and briefly mentioned the fact of a fixed nucleoplasmic ratio. We have seen how R. Hertwig derived it independently from his *Paramecium* work. Now Boveri analyzed the problem in the simple but brilliant way characteristic of his approach. He produced haploid, diploid, triploid, and tetraploid sea urchin larvae and also composites and showed that nuclear and cell size are proportional to the number of chromosome sets. He also showed that larvae or sectors of identical size, controlled by the volume of the original egg, are composed of different numbers of cells inversely proportional to the size of the cells, which is controlled by the chromosome number. This paper is again a perfect example of Boveri's art of experimentation, depth of analysis, and power of clear and logical presentation.

In between these great landmarks fall many papers of great importance though of a more specialized nature. I mention only the work on the polarity of the sea urchin egg, the monograph on the centrosomes, the analysis of the gynandromorphs, the paper on the sex chromosomes of hermaphroditic nematodes, and the pamphlet on the chromosome theory of cancer. Boveri's share in the work of his students, Spemann, Baltzer, von Ubisch, von Baehr, A. Gulick, Zarnik, and others, can only be guessed from the fact that such work dealt with problems which were dear to Boveri himself. Only one further major piece of work should be mentioned, because it seems to, though it does not actually, fall out of the frame of Boveri's interests. This is another classic: his discovery of the nephridia of *Amphioxus*. Many zoologists and embryologists had tried in vain to find a kidney system in this lowest member of the chordates. By a logical analysis of the aberrant features of the organization of *Amphioxus*, the topography of the peribranchial cavity, Boveri concluded upon where to look for nephridia and found the primitive, wormlike nephridia with their strange solenocytes. This again is a paper which every young zoologist should be made to read because of its perfection in observation, description, analysis, and presentation. Like all of Boveri's papers it is illustrated with beautiful lithographs after his perfect drawings.

All this work is witness to the rare combination of abilities which made Boveri the great pioneer he was. He was a keen observer who did not miss any detail but kept it stored in his mind, to return to it in time. He discerned at once what was important in his observations and likely to lead to further insight. He saw where experiments could begin and quickly devised a simple but efficient approach. Most of his experiments were like Columbus' egg and did not require complicated techniques. Where he found natural experiments, i.e., typical abnormalities, he made efficient use of them. But he was also ready to use advanced gadgets when he thought that his experiments called for them. Thus in his *Ascaris* work he used Tchachotin's apparatus for micro-operation with beams of ultraviolet light. He himself once expressed his attitude toward techniques thus: "Some people think that it is not a real experiment if no sections have been made, or a new stuff injected into the material, or a new gadget has been built. But the essence of experimentation is that one knows with certainty that certain typical conditions have been changed in a definite way. It does not matter whether the experimenter or nature makes these changes. Actually the scientist will prefer what nature did without man's crude methods of interfering with the material."

But observation and experiments alone did not satisfy him. He felt the need of analyzing his results down to the last consequences and exhausting all possibilities of application to the great problems of the time. Thus all his papers had a philosophical background and went as far in theorizing as he thought safe. Once he wrote that he did not like "to renounce the surrounding atmosphere of hypothesis, without which all facts remain dead." I have already pointed to the beauty and logical strength of his writing, which made it an intellectual and esthetic pleasure to follow his thoughts. Two of his published orations, the obituary of Dohrn and his address as rector of the university on the organisms as historical beings, are masterpieces of diction and concentrated logical writing. This combination of abilities, in addition to Boveri's personality, was probably what attracted the very reserved E. B. Wilson, who in many respects had a mind of the same general type. Wilson had the greatest admiration for Boveri, in whose laboratory he had worked, and considered him a friend to whom he looked up and from whom he profited a good deal.

At first sight Boveri's outward appearance was not striking. He was of medium height, thickset, with a rounded face and head, bushy hair, and a short beard. I imagine that his was the Alpine type of his Bavarian ancestors in the Bamberg-Nuremberg region; it might have been the type of Hans Sachs and Peter Vischer. But, when he talked, at once his great mind became visible, especially in the expression of his vivid, sparkling, and supremely intelligent eyes. He liked a good discussion, to which he brought his mastery of the material and his incisive, analytical mind. At one time he had intended to be an artist, and this counterpart of his scientific nature undoubtedly was always present and influenced his thoughts. Of course, scientific imagination in a great scientist has always in it an ingredient of artistic feeling, and Boveri was a good example of this observation. He must have been a great teacher for intelligent students, judging from the logic and lucidity of such of his talks as I had a chance to hear. Probably he did his best in the intimacy of the laboratory, as the names of his students bear witness. It seems to me that, as the years pass by and present-day biology progresses triumphantly, Boveri's fame is not only not dimmed but shines more brightly than ever.

4

"Neos Apollytai"

N έος ἀπόλλυτ᾽ ὅν φίλει θέος," "Young per-
ishes he whom the gods love." This Greek verse comes to
my mind when I remember three protozoologists, endowed
by nature with manifold gifts, none of whom lived to be
forty: Fritz Schaudinn, Ladislaus von Prowazek, and Karl
Belar. Schaudinn undoubtedly was the greatest of the
three and the one who did pioneering work of the widest
scope in his short life span and thus became one of the
classics of this science. Present-day protozoology is not
imaginable without him. I am happy to say that I was one
of his younger friends in the last years of his all too short
life.

Fritz Schaudinn

  Asides: F. E. SCHULZE, E. WEIGERT,
  L. EDINGER, P. EHRLICH

Schaudinn was predominantly a genius at observation.
In his younger years, toward the end of the last century,
he was able to lay much of the foundations of modern protozoology, and a few years later the same ability made him
a benefactor of humanity by his discovery of the syphilis
germ. All of this was packed into one decade of his meteoric life. He was born in 1871 in East Prussia, a farmer's
son, and his exterior conformed to his origin. A tall,
broad-shouldered, powerful man, with blond hair and beard
adorning the round-cheeked, beaming face of an overgrown
boy, he was a model of simplicity, directness, and complete
lack of sophistication. As a student he went to Berlin and
stayed there in the laboratory of F. E. Schulze, an all-
around zoologist though otherwise not too pleasant a personality. Among many things Schulze had worked a little
with protozoa (hundreds of old textbooks reproduced his
picture of the dividing amoeba), and it was possibly he
who interested young Schaudinn in this group. In 1894
the student took his doctor's degree and, in the usual way,
became assistant and in time *Privatdocent*. His first papers
contained the discovery of a complicated life cycle of
primitive Foraminifera. Up to this time rhizopods were
not known to have sexuality and were not even supposed
to divide mitotically, in spite of the work of Bütschli and
his students. Sexuality with elaborate life cycles was known
only in sporozoa, and here insufficiently. In his Foraminifera, Schaudinn, simultaneously with Lister, found the

[125]

alternation of generations. Soon he discovered the first case of mitosis in amoeba. This was followed by his brilliant paper on *Actinophrys*, where he elucidated the amazing behavior of the centrosomes in the center of the pseudopodial rays and found the sexual phase in the form of autogamy. Many of these and other discoveries were described only in short papers with a few illustrations, and only rarely did he publish a full paper. He was so engrossed with making an uninterrupted series of exciting discoveries that he did not take the time out for writing a full description of his data. I remember that in my student days in Munich these papers were repeatedly discussed in Richard Hertwig's seminars. A great protozoologist himself, Hertwig saw at once their importance but was hesitant to accept completely the revolutionary results because of the unorthodox method of publication, during an era of beautifully illustrated monographs like Hertwig's own on *Actinosphaerium*. But in the end Schaudinn came out with flying colors. This early period, which put him in the forefront of protozoology at the age of twenty-seven, ended with the classic paper on *Monocystis*, done in collaboration with the Polish student Siedlecki, later one of the leading biologists of Poland. Here fertilization was first described in *Coccidia*, and the whole life cycle was unraveled. It was this paper more than anything else which gave to Ross and Grassi the zoological clues for the understanding of the cycle of the malaria parasite. Without it this famous discovery might have been delayed for years.

In 1898 Schaudinn interrupted his work to join his friend F. Römer in an Arctic expedition, the result of which was the initiation of a large publication enterprise, the *Fauna Arctica*. Though Schaudinn remained the co-editor, one may safely assume that this episode did not mean much to him beyond a welcome chance for a little adventure. After his return he continued at once his work on protozoan life cycles. The most successful publications of this work were those on the rhizopod *Trichosphaerium sieboldi* and on the coccidium *Eimeria schubergi*, both classics in their field and, in this case, published in proper form. It was the time when the discovery of the malarial cycle put protozoology into the foreground and inaugurated the vast domain of medical protozoology. Schaudinn made his first contribution to this field by working out the parallelism between bird malaria and human malaria.

At this juncture the German State Department of Health, prompted by Robert Koch, the pioneer bacteriologist, decided to make medical protozoology one of its concerns and in 1901 appointed Schaudinn, again on Koch's recommendation, a member of the staff. Around 1900, Koch, who had quickly realized the practical importance of the discovery of the malarial cycle, had accepted the invitation of the private owners to carry out a sanitation of the Brioni Islands, near the Istrian coast, which were badly infected with malaria. The owners of these paradisiacal islands, the Kupelwieser family (later to become my friends), wanted to build a fashionable resort which would be feasible only if malaria could be conquered. Koch eradicated the mosquitoes and removed all infected persons from the islands, which henceforth became—and still are—one of the most beautiful and healthy playgrounds of Europe. I first visited there, immediately after Koch's sanitation, when the islands were still in their natural condition, far preferable to the later "improvements" when hotels, wharves, and formal gardens replaced the idyllic beauty. I think this was the first example of a complete sanitation of a malaria-infested area, and it was made possible by the insular isolation and the private ownership, which permitted complete eradication of mosquitoes and removal of carriers. This successful work attracted Koch's interest to the entire region, the western Adriatic coast of Istria, where malaria was rampant, and he recommended to the German health department to start there an experiment of malaria sanitation under standard conditions, i.e., without the specific advantages of the Brioni Islands. Right there in Rovigno was located a privately owned zoological station which furnished material to the aquarium of the Berlin Zoo and was also accessible to visiting zoologists. It was easy to rent laboratory space here, and thus Schaudinn went for a number of years to Rovigno, where he accomplished an immense amount of work. It was here that I was his daily companion for a couple of months and became his admirer and younger friend.

Though he ranged in these years over all of protozoology, his official work was the malaria sanitation. This experiment was carried out in a small, isolated community of the native Yugoslavs north of Rovigno, at that time Austrian territory. Here a deep fjord, no broader than a river, cuts into the mountainous coast, the Cul di Leme, and some distance inside on top of a hill the badly infected village was located. It was accessible only by traveling on the small laboratory steamer far into the fjord and then climbing the hill on a footpath, which I did repeatedly, accompanying Schaudinn on his inspection trips. If I remember well, the sanitation was completely successful, at least as long as the work lasted. One of these trips is especially vivid in my memory because it had an amusing background and ending. The health department had sent out to Rovigno one of their big bureaucrats, a privy councilor, to inspect and check upon the progress of Schaudinn's work. He was the prototype of the Prussian bureaucrat, stiff, conceited, remote, and class conscious. Life at the station was of course completely informal. But the bureaucrat made it a point to appear at the common dinner table in a stiff Prince Albert coat and all the trimmings, and poor Schaudinn was forced to dress and to talk politely to the big boss. We, a group of young students who loved and admired the jolly and natural Schaudinn, resented the arrogance of the bureaucrat, whom we considered far inferior to our hero, and we decided to show our feelings by dressing for dinner as sloppily as possible. But our real chance came when Schaudinn was to take the boss to the malaria village, an excursion which we were permitted to join. After the visit we painted to the councilor and his aide in glowing colors another way of returning to Rovigno by land via a scenic hike from the fjord to the next railway station high above the sea and six to eight miles distant. It was actually a beautiful scenic road which we had walked repeatedly. But what we did not mention was that after the preceding rains the steep and narrow path would be transformed into a torrent. So we put the privy councilor and his aide ashore and returned by boat. Late at night the poor bedraggled wanderers returned, completely wet, their urban shoes and clothes covered with mud, and certainly not in the best of humor. It was a mean trick to play on the elderly bureaucrat, but we youngsters felt that he had deserved it by treating the great Schaudinn like hired help. I must confess that bureaucrats are still my pet dislike, and I consider them the most expendable members of society.

During these few years at Rovigno, Schaudinn, who had an immense power for work, accomplished what would have been enough for another's lifetime. He discovered the cause of the dangerous recidives in malaria. He wrote his famous papers on coccidia, trypanosomes, and spirochetes. He made excursions to Herzegovina to study spirochete diseases carried by bedbugs. (Many years later I visited his hunting grounds in Mostar, and I can affirm that here was a bedbug paradise.) Finally he discovered the dysentery amoeba, which he called *Entamoeba histolytica*, and showed how to distinguish it from the harmless *Amoeba coli*. Not all of this tremendous amount of work stood the test of time; his findings on relations between trypanosomes and spirochetes, for example, turned out to be due to mixed infections. But his discoveries as well as his errors, excusable in pioneer work, gave an immense stimulus to medical protozoology.

My early experience with amoebae, acquired from Schaudinn, helped me many years later when I was traveling in China and acquired an infection which behaved very much like amoebiasis. In Tientsin I consulted a German physician who told me without a microscopic examination that it was amoebiasis and prescribed the then fashionable remedy. I did not trust this flimsy diagnosis, however, and went to a Russian doctor who had been recommended as a physician with a scientific outlook. Indeed, he made a microscopic examination and showed me under his microscope the amoeba, pointing out the features which, he said, made them with certainty real *histolytica*. But I remembered what I had learned from Schaudinn and saw that he had confused in his mind the diagnostic features and was actually showing me the harmless *coli*. Thus I despaired of the wisdom of practitioners and landed finally in a Japanese hospital in Mukden (Manchuria), where the correct diagnosis, no dysentery, was made. It would make a good story to report on three weeks in a Japanese hospital in Manchuria where they tried to feed me cucumber salad and pickled abalones as a diet for a severe intestinal infection. But this is not the place for it. Suffice it to say that I left the hospital after three weeks minus thirty-five pounds of my, at the time, slender body.

As I saw more of Schaudinn during the time in Rovigno than before or afterward, I might interrupt the story of his accomplishments by a description of his personality. I have already mentioned that he was a broad, heavy six-footer of Teutonic type, looking much like an overgrown boy in spite of his beard. He was usually jolly and beaming and loved fun. His complete simplicity, directness, and lack of sophistication, uppishness, or conceit made him a most pleasant companion. The younger men especially made him their hero, and he acted like them in spite of his already established fame. He enjoyed conviviality and a good amusing conversation, and his sparkling, beaming face made the entire company enjoy the fun with him. He loved the direct, sometimes rough language of the farmer and did not care to control his utterances in the presence of old fogies. He actually liked what the French call "*épater le bourgeois*." The *bourgeois* in this case were, to use the German colloquialism, the "*Bonzen*." A *Bonze*, a word derived from a distortion of a Chinese word for a Buddhist priest, was a man in a high position who showed what he thought of his self-styled importance and acted in a general way like a fat, infallible, bigoted high priest of whatever supreme power. A great many professors, though not usually the great ones, behaved like *Bonzen* toward the young men. One in particular, a big specialist, though a small, sanctimonious, and narrow-minded creature, fitted to perfection the meaning of the word *Bonze*. Once after a dinner on the occasion of a zoological meeting I witnessed Schaudinn putting his arm around the little professor and saying (I translate the sense, not the exact words), "Come on, smart aleck, let's go to see the girls." Such rough talk enchanted the younger generation, who disliked the *Bonzen* but were not boisterous enough to indulge themselves in *épater le bourgeois*.

With this happy-go-lucky temperament Schaudinn combined a very sensitive nature which, as so frequently, was hidden behind the raucous front but came out in more intimate talks and in his relations with his young wife and children. But as a rule he had not much time for either sentiment or boisterousness, as he was a tremendous worker.

In spite of his size he had extremely nimble fingers and was a clever and quick technician. I sometimes watched him checking the salivary glands of innumerable anopheles with the speed of an assembly line. When he had to follow events in the living material, as so often happened in his studies of life cycles, he did not mind staying at his microscope for twenty-four hours. This tenacity, quickness of observation, skill, and intensity enabled him to accomplish so much in his short life.

In 1904 the Imperial Health Office called him back to Berlin. He was very unhappy with the prospect of spending most of his time at a desk writing administrative reports for burial in some files. That office was known as a hotbed of bureaucracy, where so-called administrators moved the unending merry-go-round of reports and files as an end in itself. But things happened differently. At this time the Kaiser became shocked by a report on the incidence of syphilis in the armed forces, and he gave orders to the Health Office to try to find the cause of the disease and a cure. Thus it happened that Schaudinn finally received the command of His Majesty to discover the syphilis germ, if we may describe the happenings a little facetiously. A military surgeon named Hofmann was commanded to keep Schaudinn supplied with freshly excised infected material. After the work became organized it took Schaudinn hardly a day to observe a live organism of extreme transparence which he recognized at once as a spirochete and called *Spirochete pallida*. His former work had made him well acquainted with this group of organisms, and his uncanny power of observation made him see where

others had failed. Later he retold many times how he called
in the military surgeon to show him his find, and how Hofmann was unable to see anything. He also told how much
effort it took him to convince Hofmann of the genuineness
of the discovery which, when it was finally published, carried the surgeon's name as junior author. After Schaudinn's early death all this was forgotten, and in the course
of time Hofmann emerged as codiscoverer.

This great discovery, which made Schaudinn one of the
benefactors of mankind, at first brought him much heart-
ache. When he read his first paper before the Berlin Medical Society on May 17, 1905, the chairman, the famous
clinician Von Leyden, closed the discussion with the words
(I remember only their sense, not the exact wording), "We
have heard in this place ten announcements of the discovery of the syphilis germ; this is the eleventh, and we are
waiting for the twelfth." I think nobody took Schaudinn's
side. Subsequently the entire profession declared the spirochete nonexistent and cracked jokes about its paleness
which allowed only Schaudinn to see it. The worst of the
jeering crowd was his old teacher, the zoologist Franz
Eilhard Schulze, who, though an excellent zoologist, was
the prototype of what I have described as a *Bonze*. He had
become involved somehow with a young man named Siegel
who claimed to have discovered the syphilis germ in the
form of an almost submicroscopic body, a "discovery"
which was soon exploded. But Schulze defended him and
attacked Schaudinn in the nastiest way. He allowed his
clearly personal spite to go so far that, when he appeared
at the next meeting of the Zoological Society with his self-

reliant and superior smile, the younger members present booed him, a thing unheard of in German science. He never showed up again. But slowly the confirmations of Schaudinn's findings came in: the dermatologist Neisser was able to stain the germ; Levaditi and Metschnikoff in Paris saw it; and Schaudinn finally received credit for his discovery.

One of the first to stand by Schaudinn was Paul Ehrlich, who at once started his famous chemotherapeutic search which culminated in the discovery of Salvarsan. As this great man happens to enter the course of events at this point I may be excused for rambling off again for a short intermezzo. I have described the remarkable scientific activities in my home town of Frankfurt both in Bütschli's youth and in mine. At the time of which we are speaking, Frankfurt did not yet have a university, but its local scientific activities had continued to be on the highest level. There was the great pathologist Weigert, employed by the Senckenberg Society as pathologist to its hospital. He was a great original, a tiny man with a most vivid and sparkling face and immense wit. He professed to be a Buddhist and liked to do eccentric things like sitting on a chair with his legs folded. Another remarkable man was Ludwig Edinger, the neurologist. He was a practicing physician, but his considerable wealth permitted him not only to buy beautiful pictures (I remember a glorious Leibl, the German counterpart to Manet and Renoir) but to take time out for research. He concentrated on the comparative histology of the vertebrate brain, a field in which he became the greatest authority. Later he built out of his own pocket a fine research institute for neurology. As he was related to me by marriage, I frequently visited him to discuss his work and some of mine. The third in the group was Paul Ehrlich. As a Jew, he had not succeeded in obtaining a professorship—a frequent occurrence in imperial Germany. But, when the banking family Speyer endowed a big research institute in medical biology, he was put in charge and remained there all his life. As his work was always on the borderline of medicine, biochemistry, and biology, he was greatly interested in what was going on in zoology. When I came to Frankfurt, which happened frequently, I called on him, and I vividly remember the typical setting. His not very large office was cluttered with books and pamphlets—printed matter on tables, chairs, the desk, the floor. Only a small place was left for his desk chair and a round table on which his cigar boxes were kept. When one entered the room the tiny man was almost hidden in his chair and in a cloud of smoke. He looked at you above his spectacles with the whimsical expression of a wise old owl and then, first of all, made you light one of his big, heavy Havana cigars. Then he started to ask questions about different zoological subjects which somehow were related to the problems he had in mind, and the grotesque situation developed that the young man, instead of listening to the grand old man, had to instruct him in what were to him the doings of a neighboring science. In one of these conversations he came to the conclusion that he needed a young zoologist as an assistant, and I recommended one of my pupils. But the boy did not work long for him, as he was foolish enough to get himself shot in a duel.

We return from this intermezzo to Fritz Schaudinn, who was now the recognized leader in his field. Though no German university offered him a professorship, he had highly honoring offers from Cambridge and London, and he was strongly inclined to accept. At this point the Hamburg Institute for Tropical Disease Research, realizing the impending loss for Germany, established for him a well-paid research position, and for the first time in his life he could think of comfort for his family. Before he started his work in the new laboratory he received as a gift from the Kaiser a free cruise on a luxury liner, and he took what was probably his first vacation. He returned a very sick man. In the rush of his work he had repeatedly postponed a necessary operation for hemorrhoids. The infection had formed a deep abscess, and the operation came too late. Only thirty-five years old, at the moment of his triumph and arrival, he died.

Just as in Greek tragedy the Moira afflicts generations, the ill fate did not end with Schaudinn's death but struck his family, his refined and charming wife and three children, one born after the father's death. After the First World War, when people in Germany began again to rally from misery and starvation, friends learned that Mrs. Schaudinn was living in greatest want and misery. An appeal was made to the scientific world, which responded nobly—the largest contributions came from Japan—and a trust fund was established which could have sufficed to take care of the widow and the education of her children. Then came inflation, and by 1923 the entire fund which could not be touched was worth less than one cent. Again the friends acted and succeeded in persuading the senate of the free city of Hamburg to vote a small but decent pension for Mrs. Schaudinn. For ten years she was able to bring up her children decently, and they became successful students in different fields. Then the Nazis came to power, and these worst criminals in the history of mankind discovered that Mrs. Schaudinn's mother had been Jewish. This stigmatized Fritz Schaudinn's children, all tall, blond, Teutonic types, as so-called non-Aryans, which meant that they had to stop their intellectual work and make a living by hard labor. When this ordeal ended Mrs. Schaudinn's health had broken down, and she was bedridden for the short span of her remaining life. She dictated touching letters to her daughter, who had become a pastor's wife and who took care of her to the end. Probably nobody but Schaudinn's few surviving old friends know this epic of greatness and tragedy.

Ladislaus von Prowazek

Ladislaus Prowazek Edler von Lanow was born in 1875, the son of an Austrian colonel obviously of Germanized Czech origin. He was as different from his later boss and friend Schaudinn as imaginable, except for his immense capacity for work and his ability for quick observation. While Schaudinn was the completely unsophisticated offspring of the farm, Prowazek was as sophisticated as one could be who grew up in the coffee-house atmosphere of Vienna. He was in his younger years the typical Bohemian, in the better sense, of that time. This means an inverate bachelor, sitting half the night in a coffee house, an almost foot-long cheroot in his mouth (I cannot remember him without one), discussing philosophy and the most modern trends of literature. He was a man of huge erudition who had read almost everything. How he could combine this with the immense amount of scientific work he did even his friends could not understand, though nobody doubted that he was a genius in his way.

Even before he took his doctor's degree in 1899 with a thesis on the conjugation of *Bursaria*, he had published some papers on the physiology of Protozoa, and when he died at forty his bibliography had over two hundred titles, many of them philosophical. Most of these were very short papers, as he liked to make observations and experiments, describe them as briefly as possible, and go on to another topic. This made him one of the most versatile protozoölogists of the time, at home in every group and in all aspects, morphological and physiological, but it also prevented him from going to the depth of any problem with slow, systematic work. In many respects, however, he was far ahead of his time, using where possible a physico-chemical approach to all the many problems he attacked, though without following them up to the end.

While in Vienna he was practically on his own, as nobody was interested in protozoology, and this lack of early guidance was probably responsible for his shifting from problem to problem. In 1901 he became an assistant to Paul Ehrlich, who, at that time, was thinking of the possibility that cancer might be caused by a protozoon and therefore wanted a protozoologist as collaborator.

He did not, of course, find a cancer germ, but he discovered the fertilization of the gregarines (independently of and simultaneously with Cuénot), a major discovery at a time when only scant knowledge on sex in protozoa was available. This attracted the attention of R. Hertwig, who took him as an assistant for a year, while I was doing my military service. During this year he worked mostly on flagellate morphology and division, doing some pioneer work in this field which is still of major cytological importance. In 1903 Schaudinn, who was aware of the unusual ability of the young man, took him to Rovigno, where he stayed on when Schaudinn left for Berlin. It was here I saw most of him and had a chance to observe his brilliant mind and great erudition. I have mentioned the hopeless bureaucracy of the Imperial Health Office in Berlin for which he worked. An example of this was that he had to hand in all the empty boxes from cover glasses (from Istria to Berlin!) before he was permitted to buy new ones. As his type of work, simultaneously studying a hundred objects, required a great turnover of cover glasses, we gave him all our empty boxes which he sent to Berlin to the complete satisfaction of the bureaucrats and thus kept always in good supply of his needs.

During his two years in Rovigno, Prowazek worked on many life cycles of protozoa, especially flagellates, and innumerable papers, of interest only to the specialist, testify to his hard work and versatility. At this time he first became interested in virus, then a completely virgin field apart from the knowledge of the existence of filterable virus. When Schaudinn left Berlin in 1905 for Hamburg and his tragic end, Prowazek, who was a walking encyclopedia of protozoology, was his natural successor. The next year the dermatologist Neisser took him to Java, where syphilis experiments were to be made on the orang-utan. Here he made his discovery of greatest consequence, the virus of trachoma (Egyptian eye disease). This again made him the natural successor of Schaudinn at the Hamburg institute of tropical diseases, to which he moved in 1907. Now his work switched almost completely to virus diseases like trachoma and variola, and he started on a period of tropical travel, to Samoa and the Marianas, to do field work in virus research. He considered virus a primitive group of protozoa which he called *Chlamydozoa* and looked for life cycles with intermediate hosts. At this time this was doubtless the most important work in the field, though the real development of virology was to come much later and from a completely different angle.

Then came the war. Prowazek was sent to a Russian prisoner-of-war camp to study typhus, which the Russians had brought into Germany. Here he contracted the disease and died in 1915, not yet forty years old. He was undoubtedly the greatest all-around protozoologist and microbiologist of his time, though his nervous way of working at everything at once prevented him from accomplishing the very great things for which he had the gifts otherwise. To all who knew him he was a very stimulating personality. Slight of build, with a short, dark beard and thin hair hanging down his forehead, he did not look very impressive, but, when he started discussing any subject whatsoever, nobody doubted that he was talking to a great and superior mind.

Karl Belar

Asides: B. HATSCHEK, R. FICK

Though Belar belongs to a later generation and died before fulfillment of his destiny, he deserves to be mentioned in this group of great, short-lived protozoologists. His origin was very similar to Prowazek's, as he was the son of a Czech father and a Viennese mother. In his earlier work he signed his name with all the Czech accents which indicated the correct pronunciation as "Byellarsh," though he himself, brought up as an Austrian, used the phonetic pronunciation "Bay-lahr." Later, when he became a German citizen, he dropped the accents for good. His upbringing in Vienna was probably also similar to that of Prowazek, in the gay and cultured tradition of old Vienna. Before he could finish his studies, the First World War broke out and he had to serve as a lieutenant at the front, mostly in the dangerous and exhausting Alpine war at the Italian front. After the war he returned to his studies in Vienna but felt very unhappy with the conditions. At that time one of the two chairs of zoology in Vienna was still occupied by B. Hatschek, a strange type of genius. In his young days he was considered one of the coming leaders of zoology. His work on the development of *Amphioxus* is still a classic. Later he started a textbook which was expected to revolutionize the teaching of our science. A first, much admired part appeared, and then, still a young man, he stopped and never did anything more. He gave his lectures and spent much time around the laboratory, supposed to be doing some revolutionary work in comparative anatomy, though his friends said that he occupied himself mostly with painting and sculpturing. I met him only once, a kind of legendary figure, near his retirement age. He took a vivid part in a discussion which, however, showed that he had not followed the literature for a long time. The strangest thing, of course, is that Vienna University continued keeping him to the end.

Belar, who had chosen protozoology for his field without anybody to teach or inspire him, felt very unhappy in the neglected institute. In 1920 he wrote a letter to Max Hartmann at the Kaiser Wilhelm Institute in Dahlem, a suburb of Berlin, telling what he had been doing and what he wanted to do and asking for any little job whatsoever. Hartmann was impressed by what the young man had succeeded in accomplishing as a complete autodidact and took him as an assistant, and for the rest of his short life Belar remained associated with the Kaiser Wilhelm Institute. He soon showed his manifold talents and became a respected member of the group. He was one of the fastest workers I ever saw, with the special ability of doing many things simultaneously. He had very clever hands and a superior microscopic technique, which enabled him to make unfailingly excellent slides of the most difficult materials. He was a master of culturing protozoa and succeeded at once where others failed. He also was an accomplished draftsman, who produced a perfect drawing in any technique in the time it took another to make a sketch. This ability he made a source of some extra income. Many papers and books of Hartmann and his school were illustrated by Belar. He was in addition an excellent microphotographer, who produced some of the best slides I have ever seen. These technical abilities, together with the speed with which he finished a series of procedures, made possible his large output of work while at the same time he was helping out everybody else in the laboratory with his skills.

Belar's first work in Dahlem was in the field of classical morphology of protozoa, but he soon switched to experimental work. Most important was the work on the life cycle of *Actinophrys*, in which not only was the classic work of Schaudinn brought up to date but also the remarkable phenomenon of parthenogenetic reorganization, discovered by Woodruff and Erdmann in *Infusoria*, was found in a rhizopod with autogamic sexuality. During this time Belar collected material on the intimate structure of practically all protozoa which enabled him to write his monograph on protozoan nuclei, illustrated with scores of his original drawings and to this day the definitive work on the subject.

This intensive occupation with the nucleus suggested a comparison with the metazoan nucleus and its different type of mitotic division. In looking around for a material which suited his purpose he first tried the free-living nematodes. These lent themselves easily to culture on agar plates and, by their transparency (which had stood Bütschli in good stead in his early work), promised to be good experimental material. He hoped simultaneously to use the material for studies on the genetics of nutrition nowadays called biochemical genetics. He spent much time on the subject with only meager results, the best being the induction of experimental parthenogenesis (more correctly pseudoparthenogenesis). Finally he gave up in disgust and turned to a very different material and technique, which turned out to be a great hit. He began to attack problems of cell division using the large spermatocytes of *Orthoptera* in drop cultures. He combined the observation of the living material with direct experimentation on it, intravital staining, microdissection, close comparison of the same cell alive, fixed, and finally stained, and the extensive use of photography at each step. All this led to important factual observations and to the development of a theory of mitosis which caused much discussion and is still in the ring. With this work done toward the end of the twenties he moved into the front line of cytologists, and there were many who expected him to become a leader of this science.

There was one of Belar's many activities which should not be omitted in this sketch. Though it did not mean an important scientific achievement, it will show his great courage when it came to standing up for scientific truth. In the early twenties an anatomist, R. Fick, published a big paper in the famous *Annals of the Prussian Academy* in which he attacked the chromosome theory of heredity and Mendelian genetics, both of which he declared to be easily proven errors. Fick himself had, in his younger days, done some work on the cytology of the amphibian egg which hardly contributed anything new to the classic work of Rückert and the Carnoy school. Already at that time he had argued against the chromosome theory and violently attacked Boveri's and Rabl's principle of the individuality of the chromosomes. Boveri had answered him and torn his argument to shreds in a paper which contained also many new observations on the Ascaris chromosomes. After the war the new genetic facts established by the Morgan school had first become known in Germany through an extensive chapter in the third edition of my textbook of genetics and a translation by H. Nachtsheim of the famous book of Morgan, Bridges, Muller, and Sturtevant. This put Fick again on the war path. He had meanwhile become professor of anatomy in Berlin and thus a big *Bonze*. The current story was that, after the death of Waldeyer, the other professor of anatomy and biology, Oscar Hertwig, wanted the competitive chair to be filled by a man who would be a good teacher of anatomy for medical students but otherwise as much a zero as possible. His choice was Fick. Whether the story is true or not, it certainly shows what his colleagues thought of this man. The pamphlet in question bears out the general opinion. For example one of his arguments against Mendelism was that it leads to such nonsense as lethal factors, just as if nature could have created genes for the sake of killing their carrier! Geneticists and cytologists read this stuff shrugging their shoulders. Actually it was not without ill effect, for some anatomists and histologists, unacquainted with genetics and cytogenetics, sided with Fick. Thus his friend and later successor Stieve, who was to play a great role in German universities, followed in Fick's footsteps. He actually said, even in a recent address, not long before his death, that the exist--ence of sex chromosomes in man is not proven. As both of these men held the largest chair of anatomy in Germany, thousands of medical students were indoctrinated with their fossil views.

Belar, as a young man, felt this situation keenly and decided to answer Fick. One has to know the inner workings of the universities to realize that this was an act of great courage, as the debunking of a powerful professor by a young beginner was bound to affect seriously the chances of the latter's academic career. But Belar wrote and published in a prominent place a keen analysis of Fick's claims and exposed his complete ignorance. Fick fumed and wrote a weak reply emphasizing mostly between the lines that he was a big shot, and therefore right, and Belar a mere young assistant, and therefore wrong. One characteristic feature of this reply should not be omitted because of its historical significance. Fick was a rabid Pan-German, later to become, of course, a violent Nazi. One of the tenets of this breed was that Slavs were an inferior race. In this paper he spelled Belar's name consistently Byellarsh, thus emphasizing his Czech origin which, in the opinion of Fick's kind, meant a lower type of humanity—certainly a nice example of hitting below the belt. It did no harm then, and at the time of the advent of the Nazis, who might have been influenced, Belar was not alive any more.

At the end of the twenties Belar received a Rockefeller Fellowship and went to Pasadena with the greatest expectations. It was the first real freedom for him. Being highly impressionable he fell in love with the desert and its colors, and with his skill in sketching and water colors he could not get enough of painting it. He more or less neglected his work (on monocentric mitosis as a means of analyzing cell division), to the great dismay of Morgan. Then he acquired a car, and with his usual intensity he went all out for driving, unfortunately for reckless driving, fostered by the wide horizons of the desert. One day a party went out, a young student in Belar's car, Mrs. Belar in the next. Shortsighted as he was, he missed a turn in a desert road and made it too late at full speed. The car somersaulted, and Belar, still in the early thirties, was taken from what would certainly have been a brilliant scientific career.

5

Miniature Portraits

OUR INFORMAL biographic reminiscences, except the last ones, have dealt thus far with the great heroes of modern zoology in Germany at the end of the last century. At the same time or a little later lived a considerable number of zoologists whose names have gone into the history of our science on a high, though not heroic, plane. Most of them are forgotten by the present generation though at one time they influenced the development of our science to a considerable degree. I consider it a piece of historic justice if I present short portraits of some of them, again rambling off where an interesting story, probably known only to me, enters by chance or mental association.

[149]

Bruno Hofer

Asides: CH. ISHIKAWA, H. MIKIMOTO, M. PLEHN

I begin with a very remarkable man of whom probably few American zoologists have ever heard, though his accomplishments make him deserving of a place in the history of our science. Bruno Hofer was, like Boveri, one of the earliest students of Richard Hertwig. His thesis, describing the experiments on cutting amoebae into nucleated and enucleated halves, is still a classic. Soon afterward he changed to the field of scientific fresh-water fisheries, which at the end of the nineteenth century was only emerging as a serious discipline. Its rise to a high level of practical and theoretical performance was almost exclusively due to Hofer.

He had a very keen scientific outlook and kept close track of all progress in biology. But he at once mentally translated scientific insight into possibility of practical application. I had many opportunities to observe the workings of his brilliant mind He frequently came to our laboratory, and afterward we walked home together the one and a half to two miles. On these occasions he quizzed me about everything going on in pure science and at many points questioned whether the facts did not lead to practical application. The veterinary college established for him a chair which he occupied for the rest of his life, training practically all fisheries experts for the country. He at once started putting the fresh-water fisheries on a scientific basis. In Bavaria, as in all Germany, fresh-water fish was a major economic product. The rivers, brooks, and lakes abounded with delicious fish which were a regu-

From left to right: Petrunkewitsch, Schaudinn. In the Canal di Leme, Istria, 1902 (Photograph by author)

Chiyomatsu Ishikawa, ca. 1936

Karl Belar, ca. 1932

lar part of the diet. Away from the seashore, in the absence of modern refrigerated cars, fish at that time practically meant fresh-water fish. There was no formal dinner without a fish course between soup and entree. There were few North Germans who did not have a carp for Christmas dinner. In certain regions a trout or tench or eel was a local delicacy, in season always found on the menu, not to mention the delicious Rhine salmon, the rare sturgeon and his huge cousin the huchen, big pikes, the tasty coregonids from the depths of glacial lakes, and many less important species. The fish waters usually belonged to the villages, which leased the fishery rights, or to big estates which exploited them themselves. There were only a few wild waters where sport fishing was done. But there was a good deal of fish raising in ponds, especially of carp.

I might insert here a few fish stories of general biological interest, as fresh-water fish and fishing look so very different to an American. One of the most highly valued fish in Europe is the eel, which almost no American would touch because it looks like a snake and is known to eat offal. It is one of the rather miraculous facts of zoology that eels breed in the greatest depths of the ocean, live for a long time as transparent flat larvae in the marine plankton, and metamorphose into small eels which enter the rivers by millions and not only spread over the whole river system but migrate overland and to isolated lakes and ponds. Here they grow in Europe to a length of four feet and more and a thickness of three or four inches. They are fished with ground nets and either smoked or cooked fresh in various ways. Most Germans would prefer a dish of eel to any other fish, and smoked or jellied eel is always available in delicatessen stores. It is remarkable that the taste of this fish, so abhorrent to most Anglo-Saxons, is welcome to such different people as the Maori of New Zealand, where a specially large eel grows, and the Japanese. In Japan eel is one of the most popular delicacies, and in big cities there are special eelhouses which serve exclusively this fish, prepared in a complicated and delicious way and served in lacquer boxes with little drawers. The Japanese are probably the only ones who raise eels in masses by stocking ponds with the freshly metamorphosed larvae and growing them to market size.

Another pond fish which few Americans care to touch is carp. The reason is probably that carp meat tastes awful when the fish has grown in moorish surroundings. Moreover the wild carp cannot compare with a scaleless mutant grown in Europe as mirror carp in ponds which are properly managed and harvested. Such carp is a real delicacy and of greatest popularity in Europe. During the Russo-Japanese War the German protozoologist, Doflein, at the instigation of Hofer, took mirror carp to Japan and thus became a major benefactor of that nation. I have already mentioned the tendency of the carp's flesh to store ill-tasting substances. I experienced this once when I arrived in a little town at the foot of the 11,000-foot volcano Asamayama, tired and hungry from climbing the mountain. This place was famous for its carp ponds. When I started eating I almost fainted because of the unbelievably abominable, greasy, oily flavor of the flesh. I found out that in this silk-producing region the carp were fed with the silkworm pupae taken from the cocoon after the silk had been spun off, so that eating carp became identical with eating silkworms.

In view of this fact the following sounds almost incredible but is true. Among the many discoveries of practical importance which Hofer made was the principle of self-purification of rivers. When rivers are polluted with refuse from sewers, the river bottom develops an immense fauna of billions of small invertebrates, mostly infusoria, daphnids, and especially a dense lawn of sedentary tubificid worms, apart from bacteria. These all feed on the organic matter and destroy it so successfully that the river not very far below the opening of the sewers is completely unpolluted, through self-purification. Hofer conceived the —I should say heroic—idea that this principle might be used to make sewage disposal a source of food by growing carp on the microfauna developed in the self-purification process. After successful pilot experiments he was able to persuade the city of Munich to build a large sewage disposal plant in which the water receiving the sewage was so conducted as to develop the self-purifying microfauna. At a proper distance the plant was stocked with carp, which grew so immensely that each year hundreds of thousands of pounds were harvested, and I have been assured that the fish had a completely clean and delicious taste and a good market. When I last heard of it, years ago, the plant was still running successfully.

Let us return from this, one of Hofer's last deeds, to his earlier work. He first organized the Bavarian fisheries in a systematic way. He had the state appoint counselors for the instruction of the peasants and fishermen in scientific fish farming. These advisers were usually young zoologists, trained in R. Hertwig's laboratory, who took up the financially better fisheries career and became experts in this field. Then Hofer worked out methods of raising the productivity of the fish ponds by analyzing the nutritional conditions of the microfauna upon which the fish fed and finding methods of fertilizing the ponds with fertilizer in the way land is fertilized. Soon he realized that fish are subject to all kinds of diseases, some known, others unknown, and he started a complete study of fish diseases with both scientific and practical ends. In this work he was so lucky as to have the collaboration of a remarkable woman, Marianne Plehn, generally called the fish doctor. She was one of the early German feminists who went to Switzerland for study because the German universities were closed to women. She became an excellent protozoologist besides being a highly cultured, strong, and nevertheless feminine personality. Her main work was with *Micro-* and *Myxosporidia*. Later she specialized in fish diseases, and there was no greater authority in this field. Hofer and Plehn's book on the subject is the basis of all further studies on fish diseases.

Hofer, as might be expected, always had some pet plan at which he worked. He was endowed with a great imagination which led him into numerous schemes of applied science, many of which had to be dropped for one reason or another. One of them which I witnessed is worth mentioning. In some of the small Bavarian rivers, tributaries of the Danube, fresh-water mussels of the *Unionid* family are abundant, and they have a tendency to produce pearls, often very good ones, but not in sufficient numbers to warrant an industry. Hofer conceived the idea of cultivating the mussels and inducing the artificial production of pearls. Though I saw his experimental aquaria he never told me how he proceeded, answering questions with a wary smile. Actually he did not succeed. It is known that soon afterward the Japanese succeeded with the marine pearl oyster. The mention of this fact gives me an excuse for another historical digression.

The originator of the cultured pearl industry, now a big industry in Japan, was a businessman by the name of Mikimoto. He conceived the idea by a kind of intuition and asked the advice of Professor Ishikawa, who was a kind of counterpart of Hofer in Japan and himself a very remarkable man. Japanese zoology had had a rather late start, about a generation after the opening of Japan. It was almost completely due to an American, E. S. Morse of Salem, Massachusetts, who taught there for a few years, the same one whose pottery collection is the pride of the Boston Museum. He first brought the knowledge of Darwinism to Japan and inspired the young Japanese zoologists who were to become the founding fathers of Japanese zoology. The most important of these were Mitsukuri, Ijima, Watase, and Ishikawa. I never met Mitsukuri, who did not live long. Watase was for many years a professor in Chicago and thus had less influence on Japanese science. Ijima was a very good zoologist of the old school. I first saw him at the International Zoological

Congress in Berlin, 1901, where he demonstrated a unique collection of the beautiful glass sponges which are found in the deep sea of the Sagami Bay. He was already a white-haired gentleman who had studied with Leuckart and spoke German without an accent. I was a graduate student who certainly did not even dream that thirteen years later I would sit with the same Ijima at the shore of Sagami Bay, with Mount Fuji in the background. But the most interesting in the group was Chiyomatsu Ishikawa, a really great personality. He had worked as a young man with August Weismann, and the paper by Weismann and Ishikawa on the polar bodies in parthenogenetic eggs is a classic. Later he turned toward the fisheries and had outstanding success in improving and organizing this industry, so supremely important for the economy of Japan. The work made him travel a good deal and brought him into contact with a large part of the population. As he was able and willing to present popular science talks to the public, he became one of the most beloved persons in Japan, and almost everybody knew him. He was the son of a samurai and kept the tradition in a modernized way. He was a good linguist, full of fun and stories, a great connoisseur of old Japanese lore, and altogether a wonderful personality. Our common trips to different parts of Japan were unforgettable experiences. This was the man who suggested to Mikimoto the method of producing artificial pearls, which essentially consists of injecting in the proper place tiny particles of mother-of-pearl around which the oyster, irritated by the foreign substance, deposits layers of mother-of-pearl, forming the

[156]

pearl. In a crude way the Chinese had done this for ages, inserting little flat images of Buddha under the mantle of the bivalve to be covered with mother-of-pearl. But Mikimoto succeeded in putting the injection in such a place that a real pearl was deposited.

When I visited Mikimoto's plant forty years ago, he had only succeeded in producing half pearls, which he set so pleasantly that they sold well in his elegant little store on the Ginza in Tokyo. Soon afterward he learned to make a pouch of secreting mantle tissue around the injection so that a perfect pearl could be secreted which can be distinguished from a natural one only by demonstrating the injection core in an X-ray picture. The "plant" consisted at that time only of a wooden shed where the injections were made and the villa of the owner, both located on a tiny island at the remote Toba coast. The sea abounded in pearl oysters, and for ages they had been exploited by divers, who were exclusively women—hardy, strong, and big women, very different from the tiny slender type of, say, a geisha. A group of these female divers were taken out in a kind of houseboat containing charcoal braziers, stayed for half an hour warming up in the boat, spent half an hour in the water, and so on many times. They dived like fish, staying under water an unbelievably long time, and brought up the oysters which they deposited in a little basket floating next to them. The animals were taken to the shed for injection, which was done with such secrecy that I was not admitted, though otherwise I was entertained royally. The treated shells were put into heavy crates which were lowered to the ocean floor and

left there for a long time (how long was a secret) to se-
crete pearls. After the proper lapse of time—certainly
some years—the divers brought them up again for inspection. I am sure that even today, when this culturing of
pearls is a big industry, the methods have not changed
very much. I wish Bruno Hofer had lived long enough to
see his dream come to life.

I have mentioned thus far only Hofer's work in applied
zoology, but in between he occasionally did important
fundamental work, also, which showed his power of observation and progressive thinking. The most far-reaching
was his study of the coregonids in the glacial alpine lakes.
These fish living in the depths of the big lakes are of considerable economic importance as they are considered a
great delicacy, which means there are big investments in
the fishery rights. While studying them for practical
purposes, Hofer found that each alpine lake contained
a different subspecies of the most important species
(called *Felchen* in German), and he became one of the
early zoologists, like Kleinschmidt and Jordan, to realize
the importance of subspecific evolution in adaptation to
specific ecological niches.

This remarkable man, who certainly deserves friendly
commemoration, was very different from the usual professor as a personality. There was no ivory tower for him,
and I do not think that erudition, philosophy, or estheti-
cism meant anything to him. He stood solidly with both
feet on the ground. His big, tall frame carried a friendly
head, which might have been that of a jovial country parson. He was the personification of optimism, always full

of imagination, making great plans and not believing in obstacles. Thus he carried away those around him with his enthusiasm and succeeded in convincing skeptics, all of which enabled him to organize the projects I have mentioned and many others. I once had occasion to watch his abilities when he exercised them in my own interest. I had started genetics work in 1909, and one of my early plans was a study of domestication as one of the bases of evolution, by genetic analysis of all domesticated types of one form in crosses *inter se* and with the wild ancestor. My choice of material fell upon ducks, because the number of breeds is relatively small and the wild ancestor, the mallard, easily available. My problem, insoluble within the means and the plant of the Zoological Institute, was to find accommodation in an existing duck farm and the means to run the experiments. I conferred with Hofer, who at once had a plan. Why not combine the fundamental genetic work with a practical problem that would benefit the duck breeder, since duck breeding was a rather important industry in the water-rich province? I inquired into the methods of commercial breeding and found that much could be done by a genetic study of growth to marketing size. Shortening the growth period by as little as one week would be a huge benefit to the breeder. Thus I worked out a program including such work (essentially the type of work now done in all poultry departments) into my plan for the genetic study of domestication. Now Hofer went into action. He knew a governmental experimental station about fifty miles away where duck work was going on without the benefit of genetics, and he suggested that the provincial assembly, the deciding body, should give me the freedom of these facilities together with funds for carrying out the practical side of the work. I handed my request to the assembly, and after some time Hofer and I were invited to explain our plan to them. First I tried to explain by means of charts the meaning and consequences of Mendel's laws to the provincial politicians, most of them farmer representatives belonging to the Catholic (Centrist) party. Then Hofer explained the practical side of the problem with such enthusiasm and persuasive fire that the good assemblymen almost saw the bigger, better, and cheaper ducklings on their tables. Unanimously they voted my grant. It was not my fault that in the end this public money was wasted. When, after five years of work on a pretty large scale, the time came to harvest the first results (one first paper on growth had been published), the First World War broke out. My specimens had been taken to Berlin, where the new Kaiser Wilhelm Institute had provided beautiful experimental pens. But I was far away, the ducks went into the cooking pots, and when I returned inflation made it impossible to start again. When finally, fifteen years after our talks to the assemblymen, it again became possible to work with ducks, my own time was more than occupied with other problems, and the splendid facilities remained unused until, if I am correctly informed, the occupation authorities after the Second World War made a swimming pool out of the remnants. Hofer did not live to see the breakdown of what he had helped to initiate.

Richard Semon

Asides: O. PRZIBRAM, P. KAMMERER

The name of Richard Semon is practically forgotten today, except perhaps by the philosophers of science, who know the great impression the work of this unusual man made in the first decade of this century when it appeared like a comet, glowing and trailing a long tail and disappearing again. I mean, of course, his book *The Mneme.* Probably few people know its background, and still fewer know about the author. Semon came from the school of Haeckel and Gegenbaur in Jena and early turned to embryology, in which he did good descriptive work. The atmosphere of phylogenetic speculation in which he lived, and especially the theories of Gegenbaur, attracted his interest to the lungfishes and the fact that the development of probably the most famous of all fish, *Ceratodus,* was completely unknown. He organized a one-man expedition to Australia to fill this gap and, eventually, also to collect embryological material of monotremes and marsupials. The travel book which he published later, one of the best books of travel written by a biologist and very good reading, describes vividly the immense difficulty of his task. After overcoming the most grueling obstacles, he succeeded in bringing back a large amount of material which was studied by himself and many fellow embryologists and published in a series of volumes well known to the profession.

At this time of Semon's successful start as an embryologist, a completely private affair ended his academic career. The society of the small university town was shaken by the story that Semon had eloped with the wife of a famous clinician, who left her children behind her to follow her heart. Jena of course became uninhabitable for Semon and the lady, whom he married in due time, but the ostracism expected of the small university town followed him everywhere. In that Victorian era people had very strict standards for the other fellow and refused absolutely to consider even the possibility that there might have been something wrong when a refined, highly cultured woman suddenly renounced the safety and comfort of her home, her children, everything, and fled into the night. Thus there was no more place for Semon in any university, and officially he just ceased to exist. This situation was responsible for the ending of his embryological work, though he still did a little at home. One of the results was that he was pushed into doing what he could do without a laboratory, namely, philosophizing.

Trying to find an explanation of the phenomena of life in an abstract way, he hit upon the hint given by the physiologist and psychologist, Hering, who had compared heredity with memory. This seemed to Semon the clue for the understanding of all phenomena of life, including the mind, and he began to work out the theory of the Mneme which he laid down in a book that created a great sensation. This was followed by a second one dealing with the psychological consequences. Today not much is left of this great intellectual effort, perhaps only the words mnemic and engram, though philosophers of science sometimes still have a good word for it. But when the book was published a great many biologists and philosophers of science were greatly impressed by the ideas, which were presented with strict logic and a completely organized analysis. As heredity was the consequence of an accumulation of mnemic engrams produced by environmental action, a basic tenet of the book was the conviction of the reality of inheritance of acquired characters, and all material which was supposed to prove this dogma was collected.

It was at the time Semon wrote this book, almost fifty years ago, that I first met him. I was giving a lecture course in genetics, actually the first one given by a German zoologist. One day a gentleman of medium build with a dark mustache and a very intellectual face visited me and asked for permission to audit my class. It was Semon, who with his wife, his close collaborator, had been living in Munich for years without seeking the acquaintance of his fellow scientists because of the above-mentioned ostracism. I am certain that Richard Hertwig, otherwise the most benign and friendly man, would never have invited the Semons to his house. We belonged to a less bigoted generation and came to know the Semons rather well. My class was from six to seven in the evening, and afterward Semon would walk with me the half hour's walk home, while we discussed genetics and its consequences for Semon's theory of the Mneme. He was immensely impressed by the work of the Viennese Kammerer, who, at that time, was at the height of his reputation.

The "case Kammerer" is still not completely solved. It is possible that he was one of the biggest fakers of all time; and it is also possible that he improved upon nature without realizing that this amounted to fraud. The beginnings of his work made a very good impression. All his work was done in a private research laboratory which the embryologist, Przibram, had established and endowed, together with the botanist, Von Portheim. Przibram was a very good scientist, with a broad knowledge and a mathematical mind, who had done a large amount of experimental work in regeneration and transplantation and written a number of books on experimental morphology which were much used in the first decades of the century, though they were somewhat queerly and clumsily written. Personally he was an unusually charming and cultured man and a perfect gentleman. If Kammerer did fake, his boss, Przibram, was certainly the first victim, though it is difficult to understand why he never smelled a rat. Poor Przibram was to die from starvation in a Nazi concentration camp. To return to Kammerer's early work, he studied the rather amazing transformations of the life cycle of the Alpine salamander under the influence of the external conditions. The spotted flatland salamander is ovoviviparous, depositing many young larvae into the water where they breathe with gills until metamorphosis into the air-breathing amphibian, which lives in moist woods. The black Alpine salamander is viviparous, and its two embryos in the uterus have their hypertrophied gills transformed into a kind of placenta. Weismann's student, Von Chauvin, had already shown that the Alpine salamander could be made to breed like the spotted one if kept in proper surroundings. This situation was worked out by Kammerer, and in view of the earlier work his results were never doubted. The inheritance of the acquired ecological features slipped in without exciting much doubt. From this time on Kammerer considered himself the apostle of Lamarckism and set out to prove it in a series of much discussed papers, containing innumerable details of his experiments, which were accepted with caution by most zoologists but with enthusiasm by men like Semon. I do not think that anybody thought of fraud; one rather assumed that Kammerer was an uncritical experimenter who worked with heterozygous material. I personally first became skeptical in connection with his work on the midwife toad. He claimed to have made this toad behave like an ordinary toad by preventing, over generations, the midwifing—that is, the process by which the male took up the eggstrings, wrapped them around his legs, and took them into the water until they hatched. Prevented from doing this, Kammerer claimed, the male copulated like other toads and even developed thumb pads for holding the female, a typical structure missing in the midwife toad. The work described all details and presented sections through the induced pads in comparison with normal ones. My own doubts were raised when Kammerer lectured in Munich about this work. He was a brilliant lecturer, though too much of an actor, and he looked rather impressive on the stage with his well-dressed, slender build, artistic mane of dark hair, and nervous face. In this lecture, and later in print, he claimed to have crossed the toads which had lost the midwifing habit via inheritance of acquired characters with the normal midwifing toad. The result was in the second generation a 3:1 segregation of the midwifing habit but a 1:3 segregation in the reciprocal cross. This was too much. He obviously had acquired some superficial knowledge of the Mendelian laws, misunderstood them, and concocted the impossible story. I then consulted the papers and, taking his data on the length of one breeding generation, I calculated that he must have started these experiments as a schoolboy in order to account for the necessary generations. The end of the midwife toad story is well known. Dr. Noble, visiting Kammerer in the twenties, checked upon the one alcohol specimen supposed to show the black thumb pad and found that the effect had been produced by an injection with India ink. This find meant also that the drawings of sections through the induced pads must have been inventions.

More doubts of Kammerer's honesty came when he published his work on the transformation of the pattern of the spotted salamander into that of the striped one, a different ecological race. He claimed to have accomplished this by breeding the spotted form in yellow surroundings and the striped one in black surroundings. Of course the induced change was hereditary. When he sent his paper to Erwin Baur for publication, this great geneticist noted that the same photographs were used to show the control and the effect of induction, and there were a number of similar slips which I do not remember. But Kammerer succeeded in explaining them away, and the paper was published. About this time I visited Kammerer's laboratory in Vienna and he showed me his experimental terraria in which these experiments were supposed to be still going on. There were hardly any animals in the cages, and the backgrounds of both types, supposed to be yellow and black, were in no way different from each other; both were a filthy, neglected gray! During this same visit Kammerer showed me his *Proteus anguineus*, the blind cave newt, which he kept in an artificial cave. There were actually hundreds of them. He had published a paper describing how *Proteus* raised in yellow light developed full functional eyes which were pictured, also in sections. He showed me also, as a proof, a preserved specimen which actually had big normal eyes. After the story of the India ink pad one must ask whether the specimen I saw had been made up by transplanting axolotl eyes into a proteus. Nobody has ever repeated the experiment or checked upon the preserved specimen. But Von Frisch and Herbst tried to verify the salamander story and wasted much time with carefully set up experiment which were stopped when not even the simplest effects claimed by Kammerer could be found. Thus it looks as if Kammerer had joined the remarkable and hard-to-understand group of big fakers of, at some time, worldwide success: the Russian goldsmith who made the beautiful golden headdress which, as the tiara of Saitaphernes, was for a long time one of the great treasures of the Louvre in Paris, where I saw it in 1896 before the fake was discovered; the genius of a Dutch painter who quite recently produced such excellent Vermeers that experts were deceived; the second-rate English sculptor who amused himself with a wax bust of Flora which the great expert Bode exhibited and defended to the last as a genuine work of Leonardo da Vinci; the imaginative Englishman who deceived the scientific world for years by his report on travels in Formosa and his sojourn at the nonexistent court of the emperor of this island to which he had never been nearer than some thousands of miles; and finally the latest sensation, the fakers of the remains of Piltdown man. All of these and many other fakers must have been rather brilliant men with some pathological streak. The same probably applies to Kammerer, whose suicide on the eve of a dramatic departure for Soviet Russia revealed his pathological mind.

Richard Semon did not live long enough to see one of the props of his theories break down. This does not mean that the idea of inheritance of acquired characters has disappeared from biology. Though geneticists believe they have disposed of this theory forever, it is still reappearing. Apart from Russia, where it has become a political creed, there are still prominent zoologists in France, fully acquainted with genetics, who think that evolution cannot be explained without the discredited doctrine. Thus Semon's theory of the Mneme might still have admirers. Even if outmoded, it deserves at least a mention for having been a noble try in the wrong direction. Semon himself became despondent after the premature death of his wife. When, at the end of the First World War, General Ludendorff asked for the armistice which meant the end of the old German empire, Semon wrapped himself in a flag and shot himself. But General Ludendorff stayed alive, to accuse everybody but himself of responsibility for Germany's plight and to sow discord and hate among the people, thus preparing them for the advent of Hitler, his companion in the beer-hall putsch.

The second rank of German founders of modern zoology:
F. E. Schulze, E. Ehlers, L. von Graff, J. Spengel,
C. Chun, W. Kükenthal, E. Korschelt, K. Heider,
A. Goette

Asides: B. GRASSI, F. NANSEN, C. BENDA

The reputation of German science in the last quarter of the nineteenth century was based not exclusively upon the great pioneers but also upon the high level of the next lower group of teachers and researchers. In zoology especially most of the chairs were filled by first-class men who attracted students from all over the world and who were a credit to science, though they were not as great as the classics with whom we started these reminiscing portraits. Some of them deserve, if not a portrait, at least a sketch. There was one group which might be called the great monographers. They were excellent zoologists who frequently had done important work in different fields but made a place in the history of zoological science mostly by writing one or more monographs on a single group which have remained to this day the basis to which all later work in the group is referred.

There was F. E. Schulze in Berlin, whose less attractive personal traits were mentioned in the biography of Schaudinn. His most important general work was his study of the bird's lung, still the best description of the strange and specific features of this organ. Later he devoted most of his work to big monographs on the hexactinellid corals, illustrated by innumerable, beautiful drawings of the filigree-like skeleton of glass needles. Certainly nobody ever knew more about this subject. He played quite a role at zoological meetings, where his white-bearded, round face was conspicuous, and where he exercised considerable influence upon the fate of the younger generation.

Very different as a person was Ehlers, professor in Göttingen, who exercised his influence mainly as the editor of the venerable *Zeitschrift für wissenschaftliche Zoologie*, which had been started in the fifties by Kölliker and von Siebold and for decades was the most important zoological journal. Ehlers had specialized early in polychetes, and his monographs on this group are still the basis of knowledge of these important annelid worms. He was a very quiet and aristocratic man who was not frequently seen at meetings and did not easily take part in discussions. The older he grew, the more time he spent on his hobby, the collection of old prints. He actually owned one of the greatest private collections, which he kept in perfect order. I once had the privilege of going over parts of it with him, and I remember that of famous pieces, say by Rembrandt or Dürer, he had not only one early and perfect copy but a series in different states, which reveals the real expert. The following little story is typical of his poise and composed mind. When he retired he still kept a room in the laboratory, without making use of it. When he had reached the age of ninety-two his successor, Kühn, asked him whether he would not relinquish the badly needed room. He refused, saying that he might possibly take up zoological work again within the next few years!

A completely different type of monographer was von Graff in Graz. He specialized early in Turbellaria, on which he wrote his monographs which are still fundamental to the study of these flatworms. He was the jolliest of all zoology professors, never missing a meeting and always the center of a happy group. He loved conviviality and was at his best at table and as an after-dinner speaker, full of amusing ideas and never missing a good point. Though he was no great thinker, and knew it, he was a very good all-around zoologist. He read voraciously and, being a man of means, bought books on a large scale and built up an excellent private library which he kept available to the students of his institute. I do not think he ever had an enemy, and he probably was much more clever than his easygoing ways suggested. In his own way, he also helped to build up classic zoology.

There was another group of leading zoologists, who also produced basic monographs on some group of invertebrates but in addition exercised an immense influence by their all-around scholarship and their contributions over a wide range of subjects. One of the finest minds among these was Spengel in Giessen. He was one of the monographers in so far as he produced a classic monograph on the Gephyrea in which he also first described the strange type of sex-determination in *Bonellia*, with the large female and the microscopic male; this was later to be the basis of famous experimental work by Baltzer and Herbst. But in addition to this specialty his work ranged widely. We shall mention only his basic work on the comparative anatomy of the urogenital system of vertebrates, but his knowledge of all fields of zoology was amazing, and he could contribute valuable information to any discussion. In addition he had a keen analytical mind, and one might say that he

[171]

was a scholar of very great stature, though his name never became as famous as that of some others. This was partly because of his location in the small University of Giessen, where he had little chance to found a school. But in addition he had not the brilliant, imaginative mind of the great pioneer but was rather a meticulous, immensely exact and reliable, very cautious worker. His looks exactly fitted this description; he was a little man with a big head and quick movements and reactions. He had founded an important periodical, the *Zoologische Jahrbücher*, and edited it with the greatest care, checking personally on orthography, punctuation, and style far beyond the usual work of an editor. He had a great influence in the councils of zoologists, and he deserved it because of his strong character and fine intellect.

A completely different type was Carl Chun (pronounced "coon"), a man of the world, well groomed and very good-looking. He had married a daughter of Karl Vogt, the picturesque early Darwinian and philosopher of materialism, later professor in Geneva and coauthor of a manual of morphology which for decades, as "the Vogt-Young," was in the hands of all European students of zoology. Vogt was a kind of odd genius about whom hundreds of anecdotes made the round. His daughter had inherited much of her father's character and was a very original and intensive lady. Thus the Chun couple were altogether rather different from the usual type of a German professor's family and contributed a great share, as victims of course, to the anecdotal gossip which blooms in faculties. Chun had made his reputation by some monographs on the *Cteno-*

phora and *Siphonophora*. As he was a bit of an esthete, who indulged much in the hobby of painting, I should not be surprised if it was the beauty of these plankton creatures which attracted him more than their taxonomy. The plates in his monographs, of course lithographed by Werner and Winter, are among the masterpieces of scientific illustration. While working on his monographs in Naples and Tenerife, he became the first to divide an egg into two blastomeres and to follow the results. If he had not been so completely interested in marine zoology, he might have become one of the fathers of experimental embryology. While still quite young, he received the chair in Leipzig, one of the biggest in Germany, and became a famous teacher. As he was a brilliant lecturer (in spite of a high-pitched voice) and a man of great personal charm, he was a popular professor with many students. His best-known pupils were Zur Strassen and Woltereck.

In Chun's work on marine zoology he had always before his eyes the great British "Challenger" Expedition with its innumerable folio volumes of results. So it became his dream that Germany, which had become a rich sea power, should also have a real, large-scale, deep-sea expedition. Against great odds he finally succeeded in receiving the funds and the ship and was able to leave in the middle of the nineties for the successful deep-sea exploration of the "Valdivia," with many first-class zoologists aboard. I had the pleasure, as a young student, of hearing his first enthusiastic report, which he gave in 1899, immediately after his return, in a plenary session of the German equivalent of our American Association for the Advancement of Science for about two thousand hearers. But still more impressive was the exhibition he had arranged of some of the hitherto unknown deep-sea animals. I remember having been especially impressed by an appendicularian, usually a microscopic animal; this one was the size of a frog, not counting the long, broad tail. Another zoological monstrosity was a glass sponge with a single glass needle of the size and thickness of a candy stick. Then there were the host of grotesque deep-sea fishes, with their patterns of luminous organs, and many other oddities, all to be described in big monographs, the editing of which kept Chun busy for the rest of his life.

This meeting of 1899 was memorable to the zoologist for some other "firsts." Grassi had come from Rome to present for the first time his complete work on the malarial cycle, which he had worked out simultaneously with Ross —who usually is alone credited with it—and in much more protozoological detail. Grassi was a very brilliant researcher who in the course of his life did classic work in the most diversified fields, such as the malaria work, the discovery and elaboration of the metamorphosis of the eel, and the important studies on primitive myriopods. He was already an elderly man when he came to the meeting, and rather difficult personally. Though he spoke German fluently—his wife was German—he was always getting lost. Finally Richard Hertwig assigned me to him as a kind of famulus, and I spent most of my time finding out where he had left his dark glasses the last time. The short experience helped me to understand why he was so frequently in serious trouble with his collaborators.

But the real center of this meeting was another zoologist, Fridtjof Nansen, who just had returned miraculously from the years' long drift through the arctic ice on the small boat, "Fram." Nansen had started as a zoologist and had done good work, but his real love was scientific adventure. Already in his youth he had made the world gasp at his successful traversal on skis of the Greenland icecap. I was a high school boy at that time and have never forgotten the enthusiastic tale of our natural history teacher, Noll. He had made a trip to Norway. In a bookstore he saw a picture of a tall young man soaring on skis across an abyss. Skiing was unknown at that time in Central Europe, and the teacher was so enthusiastic that he bought the picture. The next day Noll called on his zoological colleague, Nansen, and found himself face to face with the fairy-like skier. Years later, when I saw this hero at the Munich meeting and shook hands with him at a party in his honor, I was seized, just like my old teacher, by an attack of hero worship. I have never seen a more impressive human being, the real viking of the myths, looking as though a master sculptor had hewn him out of a tree trunk in big strokes, without smoothing the details of the face or body. His further life in the service of humanity proved that the nobility of his mind was commensurate with that of its frame.

While I am reminiscing of exciting "firsts," I might wander off to another scene which was enacted a few years later in the same lecture hall in which I had chased Grassi's spectacles. It was an anatomists' meeting, at which Benda first announced the discovery of mitochondria. Though the mitochondrial body of the spermatids had been known for a long time, and though individual cases of structures which later turned out to be mitochondria had been described and pictured (actually already by Bütschli, in 1876), Benda was the real discoverer of the new structural unit of the cell which he called mitochondria. Benda was a pathologist to a hospital and little known. He was a very short, inconspicuous man with a round, bald head and, at that time, very timid, apologetic manners. When he claimed in that lecture that he had found a ubiquitous new cell structure of the greatest potential importance, the hearers were more than skeptical. All of them had looked at innumerable cells of all kinds, treated with all techniques, and no such structure had been seen; there was not even room for one. Thus Benda's paper was anything but a success. But in the afternoon he demonstrated a series of slides in the miserable, drafty corridor which served for that purpose, and here one saw the most beautiful proof for his claims. The cells of different origins were all filled with the typical filaments and granules, appearing in deep violet on a pale background, and excited groups stood around the microscopes while Benda, the victor, dressed solemnly in a Prince Albert coat, beamed. Nobody could have guessed that fifty years later these tiny structures would play an overwhelmingly important role in the study of cellular physiology.

Greatly different from Carl Chun was another of the group of famous monographers, Kükenthal. While Chun was a smooth man of the world, Kükenthal was like an old sea captain, ruddy, stocky, with an oblique nose and a cropped beard. As a matter of fact when he was a young professor, coming from Haeckel's school, he made many arctic cruises on whaling ships to collect the material for his famous work on the embryology of the whales, which he finished while he was a professor in Breslau. In later years he gave up the field of comparative anatomy and embryology in which he was a master and turned, strangely enough, to writing monographs on the coral group of Alcyonaria. These colonial animals, seen at night when the hundreds of graceful polyps are fully extended, are of the greatest beauty. But when contracted, or pickled in museum jars, they are a sad sight, and I cannot imagine anything less attractive than the study of their taxonomy. Kükenthal, however, who in his whale work had studied really exciting problems—one thinks of the discovery of teeth-anlagen in the embryo of a whalebone whale—was content to spend years on the coral group. In his later years he became director of the big natural history museum in Berlin. This was a full-time job, but it nevertheless left him time to edit the big *Handbook of Zoology* which bears his name and is certainly the best one of its scope. He did not live to see it finished, however. Though I met him frequently—we lived in the same small suburb— I could not say anything remarkable about his personality.

A great power in German zoology sixty years ago was the ill-matched pair of collaborators, Korschelt and Heider. For decades there was no student of zoology who did not use their handbook of invertebrate embryology, the most complete and authoritative account of the subject and even today a source of reliable information. When

Korschelt and Heider wrote this book they were both assistants in the Berlin Institute. Korschelt soon became professor in Marburg, where he stayed for the rest of his life. He was one of the most versatile scientists imaginable. His papers range from cytology over embryology to regeneration and transplantation, and many of his discoveries entered the treasury of our science. They were all extremely solid, reliable observations, but he did not originate ideas or make basic discoveries which would rank him with the great. His capacity for work was immense, and he wrote a number of further volumes: one meant as a general section for a new edition of the embryology of the invertebrates and actually amounting to a handbook of cytology; another big volume collecting all information on regeneration and transplantation, a beautiful reference book, but without any attempt at original analysis. He was clearly an excellent teacher, and though very few active zoologists came from his school—the excellent embryologist, Meisenheimer, was one of them—he trained innumerable high school teachers, who certainly received a solid and broad education. Though a small and not remarkable-looking man, he could develop a great energy, and in critical times of his university he was called upon to steer the ship and was successful. He was the prototype of an excellent all-around professor who had everything except brilliance.

Almost the opposite pole was represented by the co-author of the big book, Heider. He was a slow worker and a perfectionist and therefore produced only a small part of the quantity of work Korschelt put out. Though his early work on insect development is a classic, he accomplished not much of great importance in research. His success—he became professor in Berlin after many years in the tiny Austrian university of Innsbruck—was based mostly on the strength of his personality. A native of Austria, endowed with the charm so frequently found there, he had a noble, aristocratic bearing with a fine head on his slim, tall body. His scholarship was immense in zoology as well as in botany, and he was a highly erudite, philosophically trained man. His understanding and knowledge were always in the forefront of progress, and he was a clear thinker when it came to analyzing factual results. This quality came out best in personal discussions but is also clearly visible in the volume on experimental embryology which he contributed to the unfinished second edition of Korschelt-Heider. It was probably the work on an unpublished volume which kept him from more research work. His health was not as robust as Korschelt's, and his subtle and sensitive mind and scientific caution made him a slow worker. Here is the case of a really great man whose greatness was almost unknown except to his large circle of friends.

Another niche in the pantheon of early German zoologists should be reserved for A. Goette. In the last quarter of the nineteenth century he produced one of the classics of vertebrate embryology, his monograph on the development of the fire-bellied toad, *Bombinator*. With his keen and skeptical mind he tore to pieces Haeckel's contemporaneous phylogenetic speculations, especially the law of recapitulation. Haeckel became so incensed that he wrote a special polemic pamphlet in which he tried to ridicule Goette, who was introduced as the *Unkenforscher*. (The malice of this cannot be translated. *Unke* is the German name for *Bombinator*, taken from its call, "oonk, oonk." But the name *Unke* is also used to designate an old crank who always predicts disaster.) In his later work Goette did nothing extraordinary, though he was an extremely intelligent person. He came from one of the Baltic provinces and spoke that typical Baltic German which has a pronunciation akin to Russian. A tall, thin man with a high-domed head and a deeply lined face surrounded by whiskers, he was a brilliant conversationalist who loved biting humor even if it was at his own expense. We once heard him answer Chun and von Graff, both admirers of the fair sex, when they teased him for getting married in advanced years, when he was a professor in Strasbourg, to a young lady. "What could I do?" he said. "I had Miss ——— for an assistant. She was a very poor assistant, but I could not get rid of her. So finally nothing was left to me in order to remove her from the laboratory but to marry her." Here is another brilliant man who, after one great start, did not continue in his first line of research, though at that time the demands upon a professor's time were rather light.

The great physicist Ernst Mach once wrote: "When estimating the importance of a scholar the decisive point will be what new use he has made of old insights and under what degree of opposition of his contemporaries and successors his views have obtained." If we accept this criterion, only the very few greatest pioneers could be counted as men of importance. But the progress of science needs not only the rare genius who in one leap covers a large step in the ascent to the summit but also the slow, continuous walkers, pushing up in small but certain steps. This fact may be invoked as a justification for reminiscing not only of the very great but also of the near great, and of a few others, remarkable for one reason or another, even if only for having crossed my own path and having become a part of my own life. With this excuse for my unsystematic rambling, I finish these notes.

RICHARD B. GOLDSCHMIDT, *one of the last of the dynasty of zoologists founded by the great Johannes Müller, was born in Frankfurt am Main. Educated at Heidelberg and Munich, he has been Director of the Kaiser Wilhelm Institute for Biological Research at Berlin, Professor of Zoology at the Imperial University of Tokyo, and, from 1936 to 1948, Professor of Zoology at the University of California, where he is now Professor Emeritus. He has lectured all over the world, and is the author of seventeen books and innumerable papers, mostly in the fields of cytology, genetics, and evolution.*